Youth

LINK

FOURTH EDITION

Work Experience / Summer Jobs

Learning Opportunities

Career Planning Information

Youth Employment Strategy / Stratégie emploi jeunesse

Canada

Youth Link is produced by the Communications Branch of Human Resources Development Canada as part of the Government of Canada's Youth Employment Strategy.

To obtain additional copies, write — indicating catalogue number Y-002-03-00E

Human Resources Development Canada
Public Enquiries Centre
Hull, PQ K1A 0J9
Fax: (819) 953-7260

or call the Government of Canada's Youth Info Line at
1 800 935-5555.

This publication can be obtained in alternative formats through InfoTouch. Call 1 800 788-8282 on a Touch-Tone phone or through a teletypewriter (TTY). Requested documents are automatically produced in the format selected and mailed directly to the caller.

Aussi disponible en français sous le titre Connexion jeunesse.

YOUTH LINK

A resource booklet for 15 to 30 year olds as well as career counsellors, parents, educators, employers and community groups

Are you looking for some information on a summer job? Perhaps you are thinking of going overseas to get work experience. Maybe you're a student and a work placement interests you. The cost of receiving a post-secondary education is rising, and you are wondering where to go for a Canada Student Loan. Look no further, *Youth Link* is for you!!

Developed through Canada's Youth Employment Strategy, *Youth Link* is the perfect tool to help you find the program that fits your needs. There are over 250 programs, services and resources listed in this publication, making *Youth Link* a gold mine of information to help you make the transition from school to work and get your first job.

User-friendly, *Youth Link* will answer a lot of your questions. Phone numbers, postal and e-mail addresses, and other information are provided to help make your search easier.

You can also find *Youth Link* on the Youth Employment Strategy Web site at *www.youth.gc.ca/YES*.

Have ideas for improving *Youth Link*? Comments? Let us know! Fill out the feedback sheet at the end of the book and send it back to us. We'll send you a complimentary Youth Employment Strategy momento as our way of saying thanks.

For information on Government of Canada programs and services that help employers and human resource professionals hire young people, take a look at *Employer Link*, a relatively new publication developed just for this purpose. For a free copy, call 1 800 935-5555.

Table of Contents

Youth Employment Strategy | Stratégie emploi jeunesse

The Youth Employment Strategy is the Government of Canada's action plan to help young Canadians access career information, learning opportunities and work experience. Canada's Youth Employment Strategy provides young people with information and opportunities to help them get the skills, knowledge and work experience they need for a successful career. The Strategy also assists employers who hire youth.

Canada's Youth Employment Strategy brings together a number of existing Government of Canada programs and services for youth. The Strategy also creates new youth programs and services through partnerships with business, labour, industry, non-profit organizations, communities and other levels of government.

The age requirements for Canada's Youth Employment Strategy programs may vary. However, youth are usually between 15 and 30 years of age.

Youth Link is a key element of Canada's Youth Employment Strategy. It provides a one-stop access to information on all of the Government of Canada's career- and employment-related programs, services and resources for youth. You can also find *Youth Link* on the Youth Employment Strategy Web site at:

www.youth.gc.ca/YES

Awards, Bursaries, Fellowships, Grants, Scholarships

Aboriginal Veterans Scholarship Trust

The Aboriginal Veterans Scholarship Trust is available to all Aboriginal post-secondary education students, including First Nations, Inuit and Métis. Preference may be given to descendants of Aboriginal veterans.

Scholarships are available to students enrolled full-time in post-secondary programs of two or more academic years. Students must be enrolled in recognized Canadian post-secondary educational institutions, including technical institutes, colleges, CEGEPs and universities. Study outside of Canada is eligible for consideration provided the student is studying at the master's level or beyond.

Eligible applicants must have been accepted in a program of study and must have maintained acceptable academic standards in accordance with the requirements of the post-secondary educational institution.

For more information, please contact:

National Aboriginal Achievement Foundation
70 Yorkville Avenue, Suite 33A
Toronto, ON M5R 1B9
Tel: *(416) 926-0775*
Fax: *(416) 926-7554*
E-mail: *naaf@istar.ca*
Web site: *www.naaf.ca*

 # A Canadian Window on International Development Award

The International Development Research Centre (IDRC) offers this award in recognition of the challenges posed in defining "international development" in a world that continues to change dramatically. It is offered for doctoral research that explores the relationship between Canadian aid, trade, immigration and diplomatic policy, and international development and the alleviation of global poverty.

Proposals must indicate comparative research in both Canada and a developing region of the world with a goal of better understanding the common, interrelated problem/issue identified for in-depth study.

Applicants must:

- hold Canadian citizenship or permanent residency status,
- be registered at a Canadian university, and
- be conducting the proposed research for a doctoral dissertation.

The award, up to a maximum of $20 000 per year, covers justifiable field research expenses. **Applications are available** at university graduate departments. You can also contact the IDRC for a brochure on the award, or visit our Web site.

International Development Research Centre
Centre Training and Awards Unit
PO Box 8500
Ottawa, ON K1G 3H9
Tel: *(613) 236-6163* ext. 2098
Fax: *(613) 563-0815*
E-mail: *cta@idrc.ca*
Web site: *www.idrc.ca/awards*

AGF Financial Life Skills Scholarship Program

AGF offers 40 scholarships to encourage high-school/CEGEP students to pursue their post-secondary studies. For the first year of studies, the award is valued at $1000. During the subsequent three-year period, receipt of the total amount of $1080 annually is contingent on the student remaining in a university or college program.

Candidates must be Canadian citizens or permanent residents and be graduating from their last year of high school (and/or CEGEP in Quebec) with a 75% average in their final and next-to-final year courses. They must also have demonstrated some involvement in any of the following areas: community leadership, extracurricular activities, special projects, volunteer service, outside interests or hobbies, and career and educational objectives.

Applications are due May 28. **For more information** and application forms, contact your high-school/CEGEP guidance counsellor or teacher, or call the AGF Financial Life Skills hotline.

Hotline: *1 888 642-4157* (toll-free)

AGROPOLIS: International Graduate Research Awards in Urban Agriculture

AGROPOLIS is a new awards program that supports innovative master's- and doctoral-level research. It aims to add to the body of knowledge on urban and peri-urban agriculture, and thereby to support interventions that address critical areas in the industry.

The program supports graduate-level field research that is designed and implemented in collaboration with non-academic partners. As the end-users of the research, these international, national or local partners will be actively engaged in sectors of development in which urban agriculture can make a contribution. These partners could include, for example, community-based organizations, city councils and departments, national governments, and multilateral development agencies.

The award will cover justifiable field research expenses to a maximum of CAD$20 000 per year.

Award tenure corresponds to the period of field research, normally no less than three months and no more than twelve months.

Fully documented applications must be received before December 31 of the current year.

For more information, contact the International Development Research Centre for a brochure on the awards program, or visit the Web site for full details.

AGROPOLIS
International Graduate Research Awards in Urban Agriculture
International Development Research Centre
PO Box 8500
Ottawa, ON K1G 3H9
Tel: *(613) 236-6163* ext. 2040
Fax: *(613) 567-7749*
E-mail: *AGROPOLIS@idrc.ca*
Web site: *www.idrc.ca/awards*

⚡ Bourses pour francophones

This program is designed to allow francophones living in provinces and territories other than Quebec to work on the proficiency of their French-language skills through an intensive five-week course.

To be eligible for the program, you must be a student having French as your first language and you must have been a full-time student for a minimum of one semester last year. You must have completed at least grade 11 or be at the post-secondary level by the time your course begins. You must also be at least 16 years old and live in a province or territory other than Quebec.

For more information, contact the Canadian Heritage office nearest you, as listed in the Government of Canada pages of your telephone directory. The deadline for applications is February 15.

⚡ Burroughs Wellcome Fund Student Research Awards

A number of awards will be provided every year to each Canadian school of medicine, dentistry, pharmacy and optometry to enable undergraduates to gain exposure to research at any time throughout the year.

Usually, these awards are held for a total of three months within a fiscal year (April 1 to March 31). However, funds may also be used to support an undergraduate student who wishes to take a year of research training.

Students registered in an undergraduate program in medicine, dentistry, pharmacy or optometry are entitled to a maximum payment of $4048 from the Medical Research Council of Canada (MRC). Those registered in a program leading to both a professional degree and a graduate degree (e.g., MD/MSc or MD/PhD) are entitled to a maximum payment of $5676 if the short-term work is directly related to the requirements for the graduate degree. These awards are taxed as income by the Canadian government.

Application for these awards should be made to the dean or program director of your institution, who will select the award recipients for the school. Candidates must have completed the first year of study in a professional school and rank in the top 20% of their class.

Information is available from the universities offering these programs and from the MRC Web site.

Web site: *www.mrc.gc.ca*

Bursaries for Official Language Teachers

Bursaries are available to education students, teachers of a second official language or minority official-language teachers. The bursaries enable participants to attend courses and workshops to improve work on the proficiency of their teaching and linguistic skills. Bursary levels vary, based on the discretionary guidelines applied in individual provinces and territories.

The program is funded by the Department of Canadian Heritage and is administered by the provincial or territorial government departments responsible for higher levels of education.

Requirements vary from one province or territory to another.

For more information and for an application form, contact the coordinator for official language bursaries at the relevant government department in your province or territory.

Awards, Bursaries, Fellowships, Grants, Scholarships

Cable Telecommunications Research Fellowship Program

This program encourages students at the master's and doctoral levels to pursue studies related to electrical engineering communications systems for video, voice and data signals, or for computer applications to cable television requirements. Two fellowships of $5000 are awarded each year. The fellowships are for one year and may be renewed on reapplication for one additional year.

Candidates must be Canadian citizens or permanent residents enrolled, or planning to enrol, in a graduate engineering degree program at a Canadian university. Candidates must use the fellowship to complete a graduate degree that includes a thesis on a topic in the engineering of broadband communication systems or computer science.

Applications must be submitted to the Association of Universities and Colleges of Canada (AUCC), and are due on February 1.

For information and an application form, visit the AUCC Web site or contact:

Association of Universities and Colleges of Canada
Canadian Awards Program
350 Albert Street, Suite 600
Ottawa, ON K1R 1B1
Tel: *(613) 563-1236*
Fax: *(613) 563-9745*
E-mail: *awards@aucc.ca*
Web site: *www.aucc.ca*

Canada–Taiwan Scholarship Program

As part of its mandate, the program offers a scholarship for university students to study the Mandarin language in Taiwan for one year.

The program is sponsored by the Ministry of Education of Taiwan, through the Taipei Economic and Cultural Office in Canada, and by Human Resources Development Canada.

For more information, visit the Association of Universities and Colleges of Canada Web site or contact:

Association of Universities and Colleges of Canada
350 Albert Street, Suite 600
Ottawa, ON K1R 1B1
Tel: *(613) 563-1236*
Fax: *(613) 563-9745*
E-mail: *jgallagh@aucc.ca*
Web site: *www.aucc.ca*

 # Canada Trust Scholarship Program for Outstanding Community Leadership

To encourage high-school students to pursue their post-secondary studies, Canada Trust offers 20 renewable scholarships and 60 one-time Certificate of Merit Awards. The Merit Awards are valued at $500, and the renewable scholarships are valued at $3500 for a living stipend plus tuition/compulsory fees and summer employment.

Candidates must be Canadian citizens or permanent residents. They must be graduating from their last year of high school (and/or CEGEP in Quebec) and have demonstrated involvement in community leadership. The deadline for applications is November 1.

For information and application forms, call the toll-free number below.

Tel: *1 800 308-8306*

Canadian Forest Service Graduate Supplements

This science and technology initiative from the Canadian Forest Service (CFS) promotes graduate research in forestry and related fields in Canada. It also encourages and supports students to carry out all or part of their research at one of the five CFS centres and increases contacts between CFS research scientists and Canadian universities.

Awards, Bursaries, Fellowships, Grants, Scholarships

Applicants must apply to one of the graduate scholarship programs offered by the Natural Sciences and Engineering Research Council (NSERC) or by the Social Science and Humanities Research Council (SSHRC). Only successful applicants are eligible for the supplements.

In addition to the NSERC/SSHRC scholarship, recipients will be awarded a supplement of $5000 per year by the CFS. The supplement is renewable for as long as recipients are holders of their NSERC/SSHRC post-graduate scholarship, usually for a period of two years.

For more information, contact:

Natural Resources Canada
Science Branch
Canadian Forest Service Graduate Supplements
580 Booth Street, 7th Floor
Ottawa, ON K1A 0E4
Tel: *(613) 947-8997*
Fax: *(613) 947-9090*
E-mail: *jkarau@nrcan.gc.ca*
Web site: *http://nrcan.gc.ca/cfs*

Canadian Northern Studies Trust Awards Program

The trust awards allow students from all parts of Canada to gain experience and develop skills. These scholarships support students enrolled in graduate and undergraduate degree programs or other courses of study recognized at a Canadian university or college.

The Association of Canadian Universities for Northern Studies (ACUNS) administers the following scholarships of the Canadian Northern Studies Trust.

Studentships in Northern Studies

Normally valued at $10 000 each, these scholarships support students enrolled in graduate and undergraduate degree programs or other courses of study recognized at a Canadian university.

The educational program of the successful candidates will have special relevance to Canada's northern territories and adjacent regions. Preference will be given to candidates who will engage in research culminating in a thesis or similar document, and whose program will involve direct northern experience. Applicants in all subject areas, including interdisciplinary study, will be considered, but the applicability of the proposed inquiry to northern themes, problems or issues should be demonstrated. Applicants must be Canadian citizens or permanent residents of Canada.

Caribou Research Bursary

The Beverly and Qamanirjuaq Caribou Management Scholarship Fund provides awards of up to $3000 to full-time students enrolled in a recognized Canadian community college or university who are pursuing studies that will contribute to the understanding of barren ground caribou (and its habitat) in Canada. Preference is given to individuals who are normally resident in one of the caribou-using communities on the range of the Beverly or Qamanirjuaq caribou.

These awards may be held concurrently with a Special Bursary for Northern Residents.

Co-operative Bursary

Arctic Co-operatives Ltd., the NWT Co-operative Business Development Fund and the Canadian Northern Studies Trust offer a bursary, normally valued at up to $2000, to support a student whose studies will contribute to the understanding and develop-ment of co-operatives in the Northwest Territories. Applicants who are not northern residents must be full-time students at a recognized Canadian community college or university. Preference will be given to northern residents.

Research Support Opportunity in Arctic Environmental Studies

Environment Canada offers High Arctic accommodation, facilities and services to support graduate students enrolled in master's or doctoral studies at a Canadian university. Preference is given to environmental research proposals in the physical and/or biological sciences for which a location at a High Arctic weather station at Eureka is demonstrably advantageous. Opportunities are not confined to students engaged in weather-related studies.

The James W. Bourque Studentship in Northern Geography

ACUNS administers studentships sponsored by the Royal Canadian Geographical Society. They are valued at $10 000 and are awarded to outstanding students in northern geographical research at a Canadian university. While applications will normally be from students in geography departments, careful consideration will be given to students in closely related fields whose studies have significance for advancing the knowledge and appreciation of the geography of northern regions.

Special Bursary for Northern Residents

Valued at up to $5000 each, these awards allow northern residents to engage in an educational experience at a degree-granting institution in Canada. The objective is to permit northerners to undertake studies in a field of interest that will further their careers in the North or assist their local communities. The program of study can be flexible and may not necessarily lead to a degree or diploma.

For information and application material for any of these scholarships, please contact:

Association of Canadian Universities for Northern Studies
17 York Street, Suite 405
Ottawa, ON K1N 9J6
Tel: *(613) 562-0515*
Fax: *(613) 562-0533*
E-mail: *acuns@cyberus.ca*
Web site: *http://aix1.uottawa.ca/associations/aucen-acuns*

Canadian Portland Cement Association Environmental Scholarships Program

Six scholarships, valued at $1500 each, are available to students entering the third year of a full-time undergraduate program in environmental science or environmental engineering. Each scholarship is for two years or until the recipient obtains a first degree — whichever occurs first.

Applicants must be Canadian citizens, or must have lived in Canada for at least two years as a permanent resident. They must also:

- have fully completed the two years of coursework required to continue into a third year of the program, and
- have obtained a minimum academic standing of 75% (or equivalent) in both of their previous years.

Applications are by nomination only. The Canadian Portland Cement Association has selected the 19 participating educational institutions. [See the Association of Universities and Colleges of Canada (AUCC) Web site for a complete list.] The deans of eligible faculties or department heads from these institutions may each nominate one candidate. A total of six winners will be selected, one from each of the following provinces: Alberta, British Columbia, Newfoundland, Nova Scotia, Ontario and Quebec. Nominations must be submitted to the AUCC by July 2.

For more information, visit the AUCC Web site or contact:

Association of Universities and Colleges of Canada
350 Albert Street, Suite 600
Ottawa, ON K1R 1B1
Tel: *(613) 563-1236*
Fax: *(613) 563-9745*
E-mail: *awards@aucc.ca*
Web site: *www.aucc.ca*

C.D. Howe Memorial Foundation Engineering Awards Program

Two scholarships, valued at $6000 each, are granted every year to engineering students (one male, one female) who have completed the full first year in a Canadian faculty of engineering. The awards are renewable twice for a maximum tenure of three years.

Candidates must be Canadian citizens or permanent residents who intend to continue their studies in engineering. Candidates must also have obtained a first-class standing as defined by the nominating institution.

Awards, Bursaries, Fellowships, Grants, Scholarships

Only deans of engineering at universities that are members of, or affiliated with a member of, the Association of Universities and Colleges of Canada (AUCC) may nominate candidates. Each university may nominate two candidates (one male, one female). Nominations must be received by the AUCC by July 2.

For more information and applications, visit the AUCC Web site or contact:

Association of Universities and Colleges of Canada
Canadian Awards Program
350 Albert Street, Suite 600
Ottawa, ON K1R 1B1
Tel: *(613) 563-1236*
Fax: *(613) 563-9745*
E-mail: *awards@aucc.ca*
Web site: *www.aucc.ca*

Celanese Canada Inc. Scholarships Program

To help gifted students further their studies, Celanese Canada Inc. offers a series of scholarships of $1500 each, tenable at various universities across Canada. Study areas include administration/ commerce, chemistry, and chemical and mechanical engineering.

Candidates must be Canadian citizens or have permanent resident status for one year before submitting an application. They must also be entering their final year of an undergraduate program.

Applications are by nomination from an eligible university only and must be received by the Association of Universities and Colleges of Canada (AUCC) by July 2.

Awards, Bursaries, Fellowships, Grants, Scholarships

For more information, visit the AUCC Web site or contact:

Association of Universities and Colleges of Canada
Canadian Awards Program
350 Albert Street, Suite 600
Ottawa, ON K1R 1B1
Tel: *(613) 563-1236*
Fax: *(613) 563-9745*
E-mail: *awards@aucc.ca*
Web site: *www.aucc.ca*

Celanese Canada Internationalist Fellowships

Celanese Canada provides opportunities for Canadians to study abroad to build their international competence and to further Canada's participation in the world economy in the new millennium.

Outstanding university graduates of proven academic merit and demonstrated personal suitability may each be eligible for a fellowship of up to $10 000 for a study period of up to 12 months.

Between 125 and 150 fellowships will be awarded, on a competitive basis, over the five-year duration of the program.

Application forms and further information (including the application deadline) are available from:

Canadian Bureau for International Education
Canadian Awards Division
220 Laurier Avenue West, Suite 1100
Ottawa, ON K1P 5Z9
Tel: *(613) 237-4820*
Fax: *(613) 237-1073*
Web site: *www.cbie.ca*

CIBC Youthvision Graduate Research Award Program

To recognize academic excellence and to support and encourage graduate research in specialized fields of study on a subject related to youth employment, CIBC offers six $15 000 scholarships.

Candidates must be Canadian citizens or permanent residents at the time of application and must hold a bachelor's degree in a related field with a record of high academic achievement. Applicants must be working toward a master's or doctoral degree (on a full-time basis) in a subject related to youth employment. Fields of study may include business administration, economics, geography, political studies, psychology, sociology and anthropology.

Applications must be sent to the Association of Universities and Colleges of Canada (AUCC), which administers the program for CIBC. The due date is February 1.

For more information, visit the AUCC Web site or contact:

Association of Universities and Colleges of Canada
Canadian Awards Program
350 Albert Street, Suite 600
Ottawa, ON K1R 1B1
Tel: *(613) 563-1236*
Fax: *(613) 563-9745*
E-mail: *awards@aucc.ca*
Web site: *www.aucc.ca*

CIBC Youthvision Scholarship Program

To encourage high-school/CEGEP students to pursue their post-secondary studies, CIBC offers 30 scholarships valued at up to $4000 each or the actual tuition fees plus summer employment.

Candidates must be Canadian citizens or permanent residents and must be graduating, or have graduated, with a minimum average of 60%. They must also be enrolled in a Big Brothers and Sisters of Canada (BBSC) agency program.

For more information and application forms, please call the BBSC toll-free number below.

Big Brothers and Sisters of Canada
Tel: *1 800 263-9133*

CIDA Awards Program for Canadians

This program offers awards of up to $10 000 to Canadian citizens and individuals with permanent resident status in Canada who wish to participate in international development through a project of their own initiative. The international development project is to be carried out in collaboration with an organization in a country eligible under Canada's Official Development Assistance framework and must address a specific field of endeavour within the Canadian International Development Agency's (CIDA's) Aid Policy.

Eligible projects include:

- field research components undertaken by students as part of their master's degree program,
- voluntary service or research projects designed by individuals with professional experience, and
- internships — or internships combined with study terms — initiated by students in Masters of Business Administration programs.

The award can be for a working period of up to 12 months.

More information can be obtained from:

Canadian Bureau for International Education (CBIE)
Canadian Awards Division
220 Laurier Avenue West, Suite 1100
Ottawa, ON K1P 5Z9
Tel: *(613) 237-4820* ext. 234
Fax: *(613) 237-1073*
Web site: *www.cbie.ca*

Civil Law/Common Law Exchange Scholarship Program

This student exchange program provides law students in common law programs with the opportunity to pursue studies in civil law programs — and vice versa — for a full university term.

The objective of this program is to promote a better understanding of the bi-juridical nature of our Canadian justice system as well as the differences between Quebec's civil law system of justice and the common law system of the other provinces/territories. Participating students will need to relocate for the duration of the exchange.

The program is currently administered by the Council of Canadian Law Deans and is valued at $2500 — with an additional $500 for eligible travel expenses under specific guidelines. It is open to bilingual second- and third-year law students at Canadian universities. Students may opt for either the September or the January term. The deadline for application coincides with university registration deadlines.

For more information about this scholarship, ask the law faculty at your university or contact:

Department of Justice Canada
Ottawa, ON K1A 0H8
Tel: *1 888 606-5111* (toll-free)
Fax: *(613) 941-2269*
E-mail: *mireille.provost@justice.gc.ca*

CN Aboriginal Scholarships

Canadian National (CN) makes scholarships available to Inuit, status or non-status, or Métis students entering or enrolled full-time in a post-secondary program in Canada that can lead to a career in the transportation industry. This includes such fields as engineering, business, computer science, communications and technical studies.

Scholarship amounts are individually determined, based on each student's needs. Eligible candidates may receive an award for up to four years, but they will have to reapply each year. Applications are due by June 15.

For further information and application forms, contact:

Aboriginal Scholarships
c/o National Aboriginal Achievement Foundation
70 Yorkville Avenue, Suite 33A
Toronto, ON M5R 1B9
Tel: *1 800 329-9780* (toll-free)

 CN Scholarships for Women

Up to 58 scholarships of $500 each are awarded to women entering technical programs at community colleges for the fall semester.

Applications are due by mid-October and should be made to participating educational institutions. A list of these institutions is found in a brochure available through Canadian National (CN).

For more information, contact:

Canadian National
935 de la Gauchetière Street West
Montréal, QC H3B 2M9
Tel: *(514) 399-5820*

Commonwealth Scholarship and Fellowship Plan

To help finance master's or doctoral graduate studies (or, in some countries, research toward a Canadian graduate degree), the Commonwealth Scholarship and Fellowship Plan usually pays for tuition and airfare and provides a living allowance.

Countries offering awards include India, United Kingdom and New Zealand. The following Commonwealth countries offer awards in some years: Sri Lanka, Trinidad and Tobago, and Uganda.

Applicants must have completed a university degree or expect to graduate before receiving the award, have at least an A- average and be a Canadian citizen or permanent resident.

Application due dates vary by country. The final selection of candidates is made by the awarding country.

Application forms and more information are available from:

International Council for Canadian Studies
325 Dalhousie Street, Suite 800
Ottawa, ON K1N 7G2
Tel: *(613) 789-7828*
Fax: *(613) 789-7830*
E-mail: *general@iccs-ciec.ca*
Web site: *www.iccs-ciec.ca*

Community Forestry: Trees and People – John G. Bene Fellowship

Canadian citizens and permanent residents enrolled in a Canadian university at the master's or doctoral level in the field of community forestry are eligible to apply for this award of $15 000 per year. The award is designed to encourage studies in the area of social forestry and is renewable upon reapplication.

Contact the International Development Research Centre for a brochure on the awards program or an application form, or visit the Web site.

International Development Research Centre
Centre Training and Awards Unit
PO Box 8500
Ottawa, ON K1G 3H9
Tel: *(613) 236-6163* ext. 2098
Fax: *(613) 563-0815*
E-mail: *cta@idrc.ca*
Web site: *www.idrc.ca/awards*

Department of National Defence Security and Defence Forum Scholarship Program

Scholarships are awarded to qualifying master's and doctoral candidates pursuing studies related to current and future Canadian national security and defence issues, including their political, international, historical, social, military, industrial and economic dimensions. The Department also offers the R.B. Byers Postdoctoral Fellowship.

Eight master's scholarships valued at $8000, four doctoral fellowships valued at $16 000 and three post-doctoral fellowships valued at $27 000 are granted. All applicants must be Canadian citizens or permanent residents. In addition, applicants must hold an honours bachelor's degree or master's degree, or the equivalent, before taking up the award. Upon reapplication, awards for those at the master's level are renewable for an additional year, and awards at the PhD level may be renewed twice; post-doctoral fellowships are non-renewable.

Applications must be submitted to the Association of Universities and Colleges of Canada (AUCC), which administers the program. Applications are due by February 1.

For further information and an application form, visit the AUCC Web site or contact:

Association of Universities and Colleges of Canada
Canadian Awards Program
350 Albert Street, Suite 600
Ottawa, ON K1R 1B1
Tel: *(613) 563-1236*
Fax: *(613) 563-9745*
E-mail: *awards@aucc.ca*
Web site: *www.aucc.ca*

Doctoral Research Awards

Doctoral Research Awards are intended to provide special recognition and support to students who are pursuing a doctoral degree in the health sciences in Canada. Awardees will receive an annual stipend of $19 030 as well as a yearly research and travel allowance of $500. The maximum period of support is three years. The award is not renewable.

The program is open to Canadian citizens and permanent residents of Canada. Only students engaged in full-time research training in a Canadian graduate school are eligible for support. At the time of application, candidates must have completed at least 12 months of graduate study at the master's or PhD level, and have been registered for no more than 24 months as a full-time student in a doctoral program.

The doctoral work for which support is sought should normally be under the supervision of a researcher who holds operating or salary funds obtained through a Medical Research Council of Canada (MRC) peer review process. Awards must be held in Canada.

The application deadline is October 15. Program guidelines and application forms are available on MRC's Web site. **For further information**, please call the MRC Awards Unit.

Medical Research Council Awards Unit
Tel: *(613) 954-1960*
Web site: *www.mrc.gc.ca*

Emergency Preparedness Canada Research Fellowship in Honour of Stuart Nesbitt White

The intent of this fellowship is to encourage disaster research and emergency planning in Canada by developing qualified professionals in this field. It is open to Canadian citizens or permanent residents.

Preference is given to applicants who hold a master's degree and who would normally be pursuing doctoral studies, especially in urban and regional planning, economics, earth sciences, civil engineering, risk analysis and management, systems science, social science, business administration or health administration. Multidisciplinary studies are encouraged. Candidates with a bachelor's degree are also considered.

One fellowship per year is offered. The value of the award is $13 500 per year; upon reapplication, it may be renewed for up to two additional years.

Applications must be submitted to the Association of Universities and Colleges of Canada (AUCC) and are due February 1.

For more information and an application form, visit the AUCC Web site or contact:

Association of Universities and Colleges of Canada
Canadian Awards Program
350 Albert Street, Suite 600
Ottawa, ON K1R 1B1
Tel: *(613) 563-1236*
Fax: *(613) 563-9745*
E-mail: *awards@aucc.ca*
Web site: *www.aucc.ca*

 # Fairfax Financial Holdings Limited Program

Up to 60 scholarships are offered each year to students in any discipline who are in need of financial assistance. Of these 60, 36 are valued at $5000 and are available for students in an under-graduate university program, and 24 (valued at $3500) are available for students enrolled in a college technical diploma program. The duration of each scholarship is three years or until the recipient obtains his or her first degree/diploma — whichever occurs first.

Candidates must be Canadian citizens or permanent residents completing the first year of a university program or college technical diploma program. They must also be enrolled on a full-time basis, as defined by their educational institution, and must have achieved a high academic standing.

The scholarships are tenable at any Canadian educational institution that is a member, or is affiliated with a member, of the Association of Universities and Colleges of Canada (AUCC) and any colleges that are members of the Association of Canadian Community Colleges. Applications are by nomination only, and each eligible institution may nominate only one candidate. Applications should be submitted to the AUCC by July 2.

For more information or application forms, visit the AUCC Web site or contact:

Association of Universities and Colleges of Canada
Canadian Awards Program
350 Albert Street, Suite 600
Ottawa, ON K1R 1B1
Tel: *(613) 563-1236*
Fax: *(613) 563-9745*
E-mail: *awards@aucc.ca*
Web site: *www.aucc.ca*

FCC and 4-H Scholarship Awards Program

Farm Credit Corporation (FCC) is committed to the future of farming. Today's classrooms contain tomorrow's leaders and innovators in agriculture. Recognizing this, FCC is proud to support future Canadian farmers and rural youth. Through the FCC and 4-H Scholarship Awards Program, we help prepare young people to meet agriculture's challenges in the 21st century.

Each year of the program, scholarships are available to 4-H members across Canada. In Quebec, members of the Association des jeunes ruraux du Québec (AJRQ) and Quebec Young Farmers (QYF) are eligible to apply.

For more information, please contact your provincial 4-H office, your nearest FCC office or:

Canadian 4-H Council
Central Experimental Farm
930 Carling Avenue, Building No. 26
Ottawa, ON K1A 0C6
Tel: *(613) 234-4448*
Fax: *(613) 234-1112*
Web site: *www.fcc-sca.ca*

Fessenden-Trott Scholarships

Undergraduate students in all disciplines who are Canadian citizens or permanent residents, are completing their first year of a university program in the year they apply and have attained a high academic standing are eligible to apply.

Four awards, valued at $9000 each, are granted and are tenable at any university that is a member of the Association of Universities and Colleges of Canada (AUCC) or is affiliated with a member institution. Each year, the awards are restricted to universities in specific areas of Canada: the Atlantic provinces in 2000, Ontario in 2001, the Western provinces in 2002 and Quebec in 2003.

Applications are by nomination only, and each university may nominate only one candidate. The application must be received by the AUCC by July 2.

For more information, visit the AUCC Web site or contact:

Association of Universities and Colleges of Canada
Canadian Awards Program
350 Albert Street, Suite 600
Ottawa, ON K1R 1B1
Tel: *(613) 563-1236*
Fax: *(613) 563-9745*
E-mail: *awards@aucc.ca*
Web site: *www.aucc.ca*

Forage Crops in Sustainably Managed Agroecosystems: The Bentley Fellowship

Canadians and permanent residents enrolled at a Canadian university at the master's or doctoral level are eligible to apply for funding for field research in a developing country. This fellowship supports applied research on how increased use of forage crops in cropping systems can improve agricultural production by farmers in developing countries.

The value of the award is $20 000 per year, and the duration of tenure is one year. The award may be renewable upon application.

Contact the International Development Research Centre for a brochure on the awards program or an application form, or visit the Web site.

International Development Research Centre
Centre Training and Awards Unit
PO Box 8500
Ottawa, ON K1G 3H9
Tel: *(613) 236-6163* ext. 2098
Fax: *(613) 563-0815*
E-mail: *cta@idrc.ca*
Web site: *www.idrc.ca/awards*

Foreign Government Awards Program

Graduate students (and those completing a first degree and intending to go on to do graduate studies) who are Canadian citizens are eligible to apply for a scholarship to study or do research abroad in all disciplines. Depending on the host country, most awards include airfare, tuition and living expenses.

These scholarships are offered by several countries, including Colombia, Finland, France and Mexico.

For more information and an application form, contact:

International Council for Canadian Studies
325 Dalhousie Street, Suite 800
Ottawa, ON K1N 7G2
Tel: *(613) 789-7828*
Fax: *(613) 789-7830*
E-mail: *general@iccs-ciec.ca*
Web site: *www.iccs-ciec.ca*

 # Frank Knox Memorial Fellowships, Harvard University

Up to three fellowships of US$16 000 are awarded to Canadian citizens or permanent residents of Canada who have recently graduated, or are about to graduate, from an institution in Canada that is a member of the Association of Universities and Colleges of Canada (AUCC).

The award must be applied toward graduate studies in one of the faculties at Harvard University: arts and sciences (including engineering), business administration, design, divinity studies, education, law, public administration, medicine, dental medicine, and public health.

Candidates are responsible for gaining admission to Harvard University by the deadline set by the various faculties. Applications for the fellowship must be submitted to the AUCC by February 1.

For more information, visit the AUCC Web site or contact:

Association of Universities and Colleges of Canada
Canadian Awards Program
350 Albert Street, Suite 600
Ottawa, ON K1R 1B1
Tel: *(613) 563-1236*
Fax: *(613) 563-9745*
E-mail: *awards@aucc.ca*
Web site: *www.aucc.ca*

Frederick T. Metcalf Award Program, Canadian Cable Television Association

The Canadian Cable Television Association honours its founding chairman with a $5000 scholarship awarded each year to a qualified full-time student. Candidates must be pursuing a master's degree in a program related to the development and delivery of cable communication services in Canada.

Candidates must also be Canadian citizens or permanent residents. Selection is based on academic achievement, the suitability of the proposed thesis project and the interest expressed by the candidate in pursuing a career in the cable television industry. The deadline for applications is February 1.

For more information, visit the Association of Universities and Colleges of Canada Web site or contact:

Association of Universities and Colleges of Canada
Canadian Awards Program
350 Albert Street, Suite 600
Ottawa, ON K1R 1B1
Tel: *(613) 563-1236*
Fax: *(613) 563-9745*
E-mail: *awards@aucc.ca*
Web site: *www.aucc.ca*

George Tanaka Memorial Scholarship Program

Valued at $2000, this scholarship is offered to eligible full-time students enrolled in an undergraduate architecture, landscape architecture, art or culture program.

Candidates must be Canadian citizens or must have held permanent resident status for at least one year prior to their nomination. They also must have completed at least the first year of their degree program at one of the following universities: University of British Columbia, University of Guelph, McGill University or University of Toronto.

Applications are by nomination only. The deans or department heads of eligible faculties from participating educational institutions may each nominate up to two candidates. The scholarship is for one year, although students may reapply in subsequent years.

Only one scholarship is available per year. Applications should be submitted to the Association of Universities and Colleges of Canada (AUCC) by July 2.

For more information, visit the AUCC Web site or contact:

Association of Universities and Colleges of Canada
Canadian Awards Program
350 Albert Street, Suite 600
Ottawa, ON K1R 1B1
Tel: *(613) 563-1236*
Fax: *(613) 563-9745*
E-mail: *awards@aucc.ca*
Web site: *www.aucc.ca*

 # Grants to Artists

The Canada Council for the Arts is a national arm's length agency that provides a wide range of grants and services to professional Canadian artists and arts organizations. These artists and organizations may specialize in dance, media arts (i.e., film, video, audio, new media), music, theatre, writing, publishing, the visual arts, interdisciplinary work and performance art.

To apply for grants, artists must be Canadian citizens or permanent residents of Canada and they must be professionals. The Canada Council defines a professional artist as someone who:

• has specialized training in the field — not necessarily in academic institutions,
• is recognized as such by his or her peers — artists working in the same artistic tradition, and
• has a history of public presentation or publication.

Artists who are awarded a Canada Council grant will be required to devote a substantial portion of their time to their program of work during the tenure of the grant.

For more information, please contact:

The Canada Council for the Arts
350 Albert Street
PO Box 1047
Ottawa, ON K1P 5V8
Tel: *(613) 566-4414* ext. 5060
TTY (TDD): *(613) 565-5194*
Toll-free: *1 800 263-5588* ext. 5060
E-mail: *info@canadacouncil.ca*
Web site: *www.canadacouncil.ca*

🔆 IDRC Doctoral Research Awards

Are you a doctoral student at a Canadian university interested in doing fieldwork in Latin America, Africa, Asia or the Middle East?

The International Development Research Centre (IDRC) provides research awards up to a maximum of $20 000 per year to cover fieldwork expenses (travel, accommodation and board, research costs) at the doctoral level.

You must be a Canadian citizen or a permanent resident. The additional requirements are complex, and deadlines vary each year.

Applications are available at university graduate departments. **For more information**, contact the IDRC for a brochure on the awards program, or visit the Web site.

International Development Research Centre
Centre Training and Awards Unit
PO Box 8500
Ottawa, ON K1G 3H9
Tel: *(613) 236-6163* ext. 2098
Fax: *(613) 563-0815*
E-mail: *cta@idrc.ca*
Web site: *www.idrc.ca/awards*

Imasco Scholarship Fund for Disabled Students

To encourage Canadian students with a disability to pursue university studies leading to a first degree, Imasco Limited offers a minimum of 10 scholarships annually, valued at $5000 each.

Candidates must be Canadian citizens or have lived in Canada for at least two years as permanent residents. They must be entering or currently enrolled in a first undergraduate degree program at a Canadian post-secondary institution. Awards are not automatically renewed; students must reapply in subsequent years.

A disability is defined as a functional limitation resulting from a physical, sensory or mental impairment that, for an indefinite period, affects the ability of the student to perform the activities necessary to participate in post-secondary learning.

Applications are due June 1 at the Association of Universities and Colleges of Canada (AUCC), which administers the program for Imasco Limited.

For more information, visit the AUCC Web site or contact:

Association of Universities and Colleges of Canada
Canadian Awards Program
350 Albert Street, Suite 600
Ottawa, ON K1R 1B1
Tel: *(613) 563-1236*
Fax: *(613) 563-9745*
E-mail: *awards@aucc.ca*
Web site: *www.aucc.ca*

International Space University Summer Session

Ten to fifteen scholarships are available for studies in the field of aerospace during a summer session.

This program is sponsored by the Canadian Foundation for the International Space University.

For more information, visit the Association of Universities and Colleges of Canada Web site or contact:

Association of Universities and Colleges of Canada
350 Albert Street, Suite 600
Ottawa, ON K1R 1B1
Tel: *(613) 563-1236*
Fax: *(613) 563-9745*
E-mail: *mprovos@aucc.ca*
Web site: *www.aucc.ca*

JDS Uniphase Scholarship Program

Undergraduate students pursuing their studies in the fields of physics or engineering physics are eligible to apply. Candidates must not be residing in Canada solely for the purpose of attending an educational institution.

Twenty-two scholarships (eleven at the undergraduate level and eleven at the graduate level) are offered each year. Students enrolled in an undergraduate program will receive $3000, and students at the master's and doctoral level will each receive $5000. These scholarships are non-renewable; however, students may reapply in subsequent years.

Applications are by nomination only, and each eligible university may nominate two candidates. The applications must be received by the Association of Universities and Colleges of Canada (AUCC) by July 2.

For more information, visit the AUCC Web site or contact:

Association of Universities and Colleges of Canada
Canadian Awards Program
350 Albert Street, Suite 600
Ottawa, ON K1R 1B1
Tel: *(613) 563-1236*
Fax: *(613) 563-9745*
E-mail: *awards@aucc.ca*
Web site: *www.aucc.ca*

Legal Studies for Aboriginal People Program

This program is designed to help Aboriginal people enter the legal profession. Métis and non-status Indians who wish to attend law school can apply for funding.

Through the Legal Studies for Aboriginal People Program (LSAP), the Department of Justice awards a limited number of bursaries each year. Once the student has qualified during the pre-selection process, the Selection Committee assesses the applications for bursaries according to the following set of criteria:

- financial need, as ascertained by the LSAP financial form;
- involvement with the Aboriginal community;
- proof of acceptance into law school or a pre-law program; and
- potential to succeed in law school, as demonstrated by academic background and/or work experience.

The number of bursaries awarded annually is based on the availability of funds within the given fiscal year. Bursaries must therefore be used within the fiscal year they are awarded.

For more information, contact:

Department of Justice Canada
Ottawa, ON K1A 0H8
Tel: *(613) 941-0388*
Toll-free: *1 888 606-5111*
Fax: *(613) 941-2269*
E-mail: *mireille.provost@justice.gc.ca* or
LSAP@justice.gc.ca
Web site: *http://canada.justice.gc.ca/publications/aeda/index_en.html*

Mattinson Endowment Fund Scholarship for Disabled Students

The scholarships encourage Canadian students with a disability to pursue university studies with the objective of obtaining a first university degree. Applicants must be Canadian citizens or have lived in Canada for at least two years as permanent residents. They must be entering or currently enrolled in a first undergraduate degree program. All disciplines are eligible.

A disability is defined as a functional limitation resulting from a physical, sensory or mental impairment that, for an indefinite period, affects the ability of the student to perform the activities necessary to participate fully in post-secondary learning.

Awards of $2500 are available for one year. Recipients may reapply in subsequent years.

Applications are due by June 1 at the Association of Universities and Colleges of Canada (AUCC), which administers this program.

For more information, visit the AUCC Web site or contact:

Association of Universities and Colleges of Canada
Canadian Awards Program
350 Albert Street, Suite 600
Ottawa, ON K1R 1B1
Tel: *(613) 563-1236*
Fax: *(613) 563-9745*
E-mail: *awards@aucc.ca*
Web site: *www.aucc.ca*

NSERC Industrial Post-graduate Scholarships

These scholarships provide financial support for highly qualified natural science and engineering graduates. The support allows them to gain research experience in industry while undertaking advanced studies. The minimum stipend is $19 300.

Students who are enrolled as full-time candidates for a master's or doctoral degree at a Canadian university, and are Canadian citizens or permanent residents living in Canada at the time of nomination, are eligible.

There are no set deadlines for the program. University Scholarship Liaison Offices are responsible for nominating candidates and administering the scholarships.

More information is available from:

NSERC (the Natural Sciences and Engineering Research Council of Canada)
Scholarships and Fellowships Division
350 Albert Street
Ottawa, ON K1A 1H5
Tel: *(613) 995-5521*
E-mail: *schol@nserc.ca*
Web site: *www.nserc.ca*

NSERC Post-doctoral Fellowships

These fellowships provide support to a core of the most promising researchers at a pivotal time in their careers. Canadian citizens and permanent residents who hold a doctorate in the natural sciences or engineering are eligible. Support is $35 000 per year for a maximum of 24 months. Applications for the annual competition must be received at NSERC (the Natural Sciences and Engineering Research Council of Canada) by November 15.

Awards, Bursaries, Fellowships, Grants, Scholarships

For further information, visit NSERC's Web site or contact:

NSERC
Scholarships and Fellowships Division
350 Albert Street
Ottawa, ON K1A 1H5
Tel: *(613) 995-5521*
E-mail: *schol@nserc.ca*
Web site: *www.nserc.ca*

⚡ NSERC Post-graduate Scholarships

Post-graduate scholarships (PGSs) provide financial support to high-calibre scholars who are engaged in master's or doctoral programs in the natural sciences or engineering. Scholarship support is limited to a maximum of four years. The value of a PGS-A for students in their second or third year of graduate studies is $17 300. A PGS-B award for doctoral students in their third and fourth year of graduate studies is $19 100.

Students currently enrolled at a Canadian university must apply through their university. The application deadlines will vary by university; students must consult their university Scholarships Liaison Office. Other potential applicants should consult their nearest Canadian university or visit the NSERC (the Natural Sciences and Engineering Research Council of Canada) Web site for further information. All applications for the annual competition must be received at NSERC in late November.

More information is available from:

NSERC
Scholarships and Fellowships Division
350 Albert Street
Ottawa, ON K1A 1H5
Tel: *(613) 995-5521*
E-mail: *schol@nserc.ca*
Web site: *www.nserc.ca*

Official Language Fellowships

Bursaries for one year, or two semesters, are provided to allow post-secondary students to study in their second official language and to enable francophone students from minority areas to continue post-secondary studies in their mother tongue. Bursary levels vary, based on the discretionary guidelines applied in individual provinces and territories. The bursary may also cover travel costs for students who are part of an official-language minority community.

The program is funded by the Department of Canadian Heritage and is administered by the provincial or territorial government departments responsible for higher levels of education. Deadlines vary from one province/territory to another.

For more information and an application form, contact the coordinator for official-language fellowships at the relevant government department in your province or territory.

Organization of American States PRA Fellowship Program

Are you interested in advanced study or research involving a member country of the Organization of American States? Fellowships are available to encourage the economic, social, scientific and cultural development of the member states of the Organization of American States. The goal is to promote a stronger bond and better understanding among the peoples of the Americas.

Applications are due on a specified date in January each year.

For further information, or for application forms, Canadian citizens or permanent residents should contact:

International Council for Canadian Studies
325 Dalhousie Street, Suite 800
Ottawa, ON K1N 7G2
Tel: *(613) 789-7828*
Fax: *(613) 789-7830*
E-mail: *general@iccs-ciec.ca*
Web site: *www.iccs-ciec.ca*

Petro-Canada Graduate Research Award Program

To recognize academic excellence and to support and encourage graduate research in specialized fields of study relating to the petroleum industry, Petro-Canada offers up to four $10 000 scholarships.

Candidates must be Canadian citizens or permanent residents and working toward a master's or doctoral degree (on a full-time basis) in a subject related to the oil and gas industry. Fields of study may include the sciences, engineering, social sciences and business administration. Awards are granted on the basis of academic standing and demonstrated potential for advanced study and research.

Applications must be sent to the Association of Universities and Colleges of Canada (AUCC), which administers the program for Petro-Canada. The due date is February 1.

For more information, visit the AUCC Web site or contact:

Association of Universities and Colleges of Canada
Canadian Awards Program
350 Albert Street, Suite 600
Ottawa, ON K1R 1B1
Tel: *(613) 563-1236*
Fax: *(613) 563-9745*
E-mail: *awards@aucc.ca*
Web site: *www.aucc.ca*

Queen Elizabeth Silver Jubilee Endowment Fund for Study in a Second Official Language Award Program

The program encourages young Canadians who wish to improve their proficiency in their second official language to pursue studies, on a full-time basis, at another university that functions in the other official language and in a milieu in which that language predominates.

All disciplines except translation are eligible. Students must continue studies in the discipline in which they are enrolled at their home university.

Candidates must be Canadian citizens or permanent residents of Canada enrolled in the second or third year of their first under-graduate university program. (Candidates attending a Quebec institution can be in their first year of a first undergraduate program.)

The program provides non-renewable scholarships of $5000 for one academic year, plus transportation expenses for one return trip between the place of residence and the university to be attended.

Each member institution of the Association of Universities and Colleges of Canada (AUCC) may nominate one candidate. Each university may set its own policies and procedures concerning the selection of its nominee. The university nominations are due at the AUCC by February 15.

The AUCC administers the program on behalf of the Department of Canadian Heritage.

Candidates can obtain information and application forms from their university awards office or by contacting:

Association of Universities and Colleges of Canada
Canadian Awards Program
350 Albert Street, Suite 600
Ottawa, ON K1R 1B1
Tel: *(613) 563-1236*
Fax: *(613) 563-9745*
E-mail: *awards@aucc.ca*
Web site: *www.aucc.ca*

Awards, Bursaries, Fellowships, Grants, Scholarships

SSHRC Doctoral Fellowships Program

If you are a Canadian citizen or permanent resident of Canada and you have completed or are about to complete a master's degree in the humanities or social sciences, you may be interested in applying for a Social Sciences and Humanities Research Council of Canada (SSHRC) Doctoral Fellowship.

The fellowship provides financial support of up to $16 620 per year to students pursuing a doctoral degree on a full-time basis. The fellowship may be renewed up to and including the fourth year of doctoral study.

Applications are due by November 15 for students not registered at a Canadian university. Students registered at a Canadian university must submit their applications directly to their department head by the deadline set by the university.

SSHRC also offers several fellowship supplements for research in health, forestry, tobacco control, adult literacy and federalism.

Application guides and forms are available on the SSHRC Web site. Information is also available from:

Social Sciences and Humanities Research Council
Fellowships
350 Albert Street
PO Box 1610
Ottawa, ON K1P 6G4
Tel: *(613) 943-7777*
Web site: *www.sshrc.ca*

Strategic and Standard Research Grant Programs

These programs encourage researchers to employ students to participate in Social Sciences and Humanities Research Council (SSHRC)-funded projects. By participating in research projects conducted by the best Canadian researchers in disciplinary as well as interdisciplinary collaborative research contexts, young students diversify and enrich their learning experience.

Contact your university department head to see what opportunities may exist to work on an SSHRC-funded research project.

For more information, please contact:

Social Sciences and Humanities Research Council
350 Albert Street
PO Box 1610
Ottawa, ON K1P 6G4
Tel: *(613) 992-0691*
Web site: *www.sshrc.ca*

Awards, Bursaries, Fellowships, Grants, Scholarships

Summer Language Bursary Program

Being able to speak both of Canada's official languages can be a tremendous asset when you start looking for employment. The Summer Language Bursary Program gives you the opportunity to learn either English or French as a second language.

The program grants bursaries to students across Canada to allow them to participate in five-week immersion courses in English or French at accredited institutions. Canadian students who have completed at least grade 11 (or *secondaire* V in Quebec), and who have been enrolled as full-time students for at least one semester during the academic year, are eligible.

The deadline for applications is February 15. **For information**, contact the Canadian Heritage office nearest you, as listed in the Government of Canada pages of your telephone directory.

The Paul Sargent Memorial Linguistic Scholarship Program

Two scholarships, valued at $12 000 each, are awarded annually and are renewable for one additional year. Candidates must be Canadian citizens at the time of application and must hold a bachelor's degree in a related field with a record of high academic achievement. Applicants must have at least an intermediate level of competence in an Oriental, Middle Eastern or Eastern European language (the minimum proficiency required would be a consistent A- in language courses).

Applications must be submitted to the Association of Universities and Colleges of Canada (AUCC) by February 7.

Awards, Bursaries, Fellowships, Grants, Scholarships

For more information, visit the AUCC Web site or contact:

Association of Universities and Colleges of Canada
Canadian Awards Program
350 Albert Street, Suite 600
Ottawa, ON K1R 1B1
Tel: *(613) 563-1236*
Fax: *(613) 563-9745*
E-mail: *awards@aucc.ca*
Web site: *www.aucc.ca*

The SHL Systemhouse President's Award for Education and Technology Program

Post-secondary students pursuing their studies in the fields of computer science and computer engineering are eligible to apply. Candidates must have maintained an honours level average (70% for colleges) on a full academic workload in their previous year of study and must also be entering the final year of an honours degree or college diploma program.

SHL Systemhouse offers 28 non-renewable scholarships annually — 20 university scholarships valued at $5000 and 8 college scholarships valued at $2500. [See the Association of Universities and Colleges of Canada (AUCC) Web site for a list of the universities and colleges selected by SHL Systemhouse.]

Applications are by nomination only, and each eligible institution may nominate three candidates. The applications must be received by the AUCC by July 2.

For more information, visit the AUCC Web site or contact:

Association of Universities and Colleges of Canada
Canadian Awards Program
350 Albert Street, Suite 600
Ottawa, ON K1R 1B1
Tel: *(613) 563-1236*
Fax: *(613) 563-9745*
E-mail: *awards@aucc.ca*
Web site: *www.aucc.ca*

Awards, Bursaries, Fellowships, Grants, Scholarships

Undergraduate Student Research Awards in Industry

NSERC (the Natural Sciences and Engineering Research Council of Canada) offers awards to help undergraduate students gain research experience in an industrial setting, to stimulate their interest in research in the natural sciences and engineering, and to encourage the students to undertake graduate studies in these fields. The award of $1000 per month (for up to four months) is supplemented by at least 25% by the company.

You are eligible to apply for an award if you are a full-time undergraduate student in natural sciences or engineering, and are a Canadian citizen or permanent resident. To be eligible to hold an award, you must have completed at least the first two years of your bachelor's degree with a minimum B average.

The deadline for applications is determined by the employer.

Application forms and lists of eligible companies are available from the NSERC Undergraduate Liaison Office at your university, the NSERC Web site or directly from NSERC at:

NSERC
Scholarships and Fellowships Division
350 Albert Street
Ottawa, ON K1A 1H5
Tel: *(613) 996-2009*
E-mail: *schol@nserc.ca*
Web site: *www.nserc.ca*

If you're an entrepreneur, or are thinking of becoming one, take a look at the Young Entrepreneurs Awards in the *Entrepreneurship* section of this publication.

Undergraduate Student Research Awards in Universities

NSERC (the Natural Sciences and Engineering Research Council of Canada) gives undergraduate students a chance to conduct research for short periods at a Canadian university. Students receive $1000 a month for up to four months ($4000 in total), which is supplemented by at least 25% by the university.

The research awards are available to Canadian citizens and permanent residents who, at the time of application, are registered as full-time students in an eligible undergraduate program in the natural sciences or engineering at an eligible institution. Students must have obtained a cumulative minimum B average, and have completed at least the first year of their bachelor's degree, to be eligible to hold an award.

Application deadlines are determined by the individual universities. Applications must not be sent directly to NSERC by either the student or the head of the department; the university's internal procedures for selecting students must be followed.

Contact the university at which you would like to work, and complete NSERC Form 202. **More information and application forms are available** from the NSERC Undergraduate Liaison Office at your university, the NSERC Web site or directly from NSERC at:

NSERC
Scholarships and Fellowships Division
350 Albert Street
Ottawa, ON K1A 1H5
Tel: *(613) 996-2009*
E-mail: *schol@nserc.ca*
Web site: *www.nserc.ca*

Visiting Fellowships in Canadian Government Laboratories

This program provides promising young scientists and engineers with the opportunity to work with research groups or leaders in Canadian government laboratories and research institutions.

The fellowship has an annual value of $36 785 plus a travel allowance for fellow, spouse and children. There are no deadlines for application to this program; applications are processed and reviewed as they are received.

For more information and an application form, contact:

NSERC (the Natural Sciences and Engineering Research Council of Canada)
Scholarships and Fellowships Division
350 Albert Street
Ottawa, ON K1A 1H5
Tel: *(613) 995-5992*
E-mail: *schol@nserc.ca*
Web site: *www.nserc.ca*

Career Information Tools

🌱 Biotech Career Kit

Designed to fit into the provincial science and career planning curriculum, the Biotech Career Kit combines edutainment learning with serious science and a comprehensive career resource.

This kit provides opportunities for users to:

- learn about career opportunities in biotechnology;
- understand what skills and thinking processes are involved in biotech careers;
- explore the interviewing process and human resources management principles; and
- engage in problem solving, critical thinking, evaluation and skillbuilding.

For more information, contact:

Biotechnology Human Resource Council
420 – 130 Albert Street
Ottawa, ON K1P 5G4
Tel: *(613) 235-1402*
Fax: *(613) 233-7541*
E-mail: *info@bhrc.ca*
Web site: *www.bhrc.ca*

🌱 Canada Career Week

This national week-long series of events is held each year in the first week of November to inform young people about their career and employment options. Canada Career Week (CCW) is a great time for you to explore career opportunities for yourself, your family and your friends.

Brochures and information material designed to help schools and communities develop CCW activities are available from:

Canada Career Consortium
1204 – 66 Slater Street
Ottawa, ON K1P 5H1
Fax: *(613) 230-7681*
Web site: *www.careerccc.org*

Canada Career Week: Getting Started

Getting Started is a useful resource published to support Canada Career Week. It provides organizers with ideas and suggestions that will help in the planning of Canada Career Week events. This resource guide includes articles on publicity, media relations, career fairs and co-operative education programs.

For more information, or to order a copy, contact:

Canada Career Consortium
1204 – 66 Slater Street
Ottawa, ON K1P 5H1
Fax: *(613) 230-7681*
Web site: *www.careerccc.org*

 # Canada Prospects 1998–1999 and 1999–2000

The 1998–1999 and 1999–2000 versions of Canada Prospects are produced by the Canada Career Consortium (CCC). Copies can be obtained through the CCC Web site or by faxing a request to the CCC.

Fax: *(613) 230-7681*
Web site: *www.careerccc.org*

Canada Prospects – Facilitator Guide 1999–2000

Practical, flexible and easy to use, the Canada Prospects Facilitator's Guide is the ideal vehicle to deliver the value of Canada Prospects 1999-2000. Copies can be obtained through the Canada Career Consortium (CCC) Web site or by faxing a request to the CCC. (Cat. No. CCC-CP-FG 99)

Fax: *(613) 230-7681*
Web site: *www.careerccc.org*

 **CanLearn Interactive**

CanLearn Interactive is a gateway to information, products and services that help Canadians make informed choices when planning and financing their education. Developed by Human Resources Development Canada in partnership with provincial and territorial governments, national organizations and other stakeholders, CanLearn Interactive offers learners free interactive tools and single-window access to current, personalized and complete information.

CanLearn Interactive provides up-to-date information on Canadian universities, colleges and private-sector institutions, career options, and financial planning and assistance. A variety of interactive tools help users create learning and financial plans best suited to their individual situations. The site also houses live chat forums and databases where users can search for a wide range of on-line information.

CanLearn Interactive is Canada's only one-stop Web site for information and interactive tools designed to help you decide what and where to study and how to cover the costs.

For more information, contact:

Jody Lobb
CanLearn Information Products Group
25 Eddy Street, 10th Floor, Room 110A25
Hull, QC K1A 0M5
Tel: *(819) 997-3410*
Fax: *(819) 953-8147*
E-mail: *info@canlearn.ca*
Web site: *www.canlearn.ca*

Career Considerations

This wall chart describes 19 occupational groups and provides examples of various occupations within each. Brochures for each group accompany the chart, giving further details on specific occupations and educational requirements.

Chart: Cat. No. Y-049-03-91
Brochures: Cat. No. Y-050-03-91

For more information, or to order a copy, contact:

Human Resources Development Canada
Public Enquiries Centre
140 Promenade du Portage
Hull, QC K1A 0J9
Fax: *(819) 953-7260*
Web site: *www.hrdc-drhc.gc.ca/career-carriere*

 # Career Directions

Career Directions provides detailed information on 185 occupations that do not require a university degree. It includes a description of each occupation and the related educational requirements such as community college, CEGEP, trades/technical training, apprentice-ship, on-the-job training and other specialized training.

Copies can be obtained through the Canada Career Consortium (CCC) Web site or by faxing a request to the CCC.

Fax: *(613) 230-7681*
Web site: *www.careerccc.org*

 **Career Moves**

Career Moves is a series of booklets with information on occupational and career possibilities in eight economic sectors.

Natural and Applied Sciences: Cat. No. Y-118-09-93E
Health and Medicine: Cat. No. Y-119-09-93E
Arts, Culture, Sports and Recreation: Cat. No. Y-120-09-93E
Education, Social Sciences, Social Services and Religion:
Cat. No. Y-121-03-94E
Business, Finance and Administration: Cat. No. Y-122-03-94E
Trades, Transportation and Utilities: Cat. No. Y-123-03-94E
Manufacturing and Natural Resources: Cat. No. Y-124-11-94E
Sales and Services: Cat. No. Y-125-11-94E

For copies, contact:

Human Resources Development Canada
Public Enquiries Centre
140 Promenade du Portage
Hull, QC K1A 0J9
Fax: *(819) 953-7260*
Web site: *www.hrdc-drhc.gc.ca/career-carriere*

Interested in expanding your skills and enhancing your employability? Take a look at the *Skills Development and Learning Opportunities* section of this publication.

Careers in a Package

This interdisciplinary teaching kit provides young people from grades 5 to 11 with a basic understanding of the packaging industry, its impact on the environment and its potential as a career choice.

To order, or for more information, contact:

The Packaging Career Council of Canada
Fax: *(416) 490-7844*
E-mail: *info@packagingcareers.org*

Careers in Culture

Careers in Culture is an innovative and valuable set of career booklets and an interactive CD-ROM designed to help youth, guidance or career counsellors, teachers and parents better understand opportunities in the cultural sector. Checklists, word matchups and other fun activities keep it interesting and informative.

For more information, contact:

Cultural Human Resources Council
17 York Street, Suite 201
Ottawa, ON K1N 9J6
Tel: *(613) 562-1535*
Fax: *(613) 562-2982*
E-mail: *info@culturalhrc.ca*
Web site: *www.culturalhrc.ca*

🏃 Careers in Transportation

A video and a guide introducing high-school students to careers in the transportation industry are available from the organizers of National Transportation Week.

For more information, please contact:

National Transportation Week
451 Daly Avenue
Ottawa, ON K1N 6H6
Tel: *(613) 244-6080*
Fax: *(613) 241-7428*
E-mail: *rcross@cit.ca*

🏃 Catalyst for Caring

This 52-page booklet chronicles the many aspects of the Stay-in-School initiative and captures the achievements of thousands of Canadians whose lives were changed by the program. (Cat. No. Y-155-05-94E)

For more information, contact:

Human Resources Development Canada
Public Enquiries Centre
140 Promenade du Portage
Hull, QC K1A 0J9
Fax: *(819) 953-7260*

> **Trying to decide what kind of career might interest you?
> Want to learn more about job-search strategies?
> Curious about which regions and sectors are currently
> experiencing growth? Check out the *Job-Search Tools*
> section of this publication for a wealth of useful
> resources.**

 Closing the Skills Gap

This career development guide provides a wide range of school activities to help young people acquire career planning strategies, gain a better understanding of the world of work and learn about opportunities in their communities. The guide also includes descriptions of programs and events designed to create partnerships between schools and local businesses. (Cat. No. Y-198-11-96E)

For a copy, contact:

Human Resources Development Canada
Public Enquiries Centre
140 Promenade du Portage
Hull, QC K1A 0J9
Fax: *(819) 953-7260*
Web site: *www.hrdc-drhc.gc.ca/career-carriere*

 Employability Skills Toolkit

This five-step guide helps you manage your own skills development. It draws on the Conference Board of Canada's Employability Skills and Human Resources Development Canada's Essential Skills Research Project.

The toolkit helps you to:

• recognize your employability skills, attitudes and behaviours;
• self-assess the skills you have;
• plan and design your own skills development activities;
• get feedback to support your own skills development; and
• market yourself.

For more information, visit the Web site at *www.conferenceboard.ca/nbec.*

EnviroCareers Resource Package

This innovative suite of products, targeted at 14- to 24-year-olds, includes an introductory video, guidebook, interactive CD-ROM/ Web site, and eye-catching tabloid and newsletter designed to help youth understand the many options and opportunities environmental employment has to offer. A facilitator's guide is also included to help educators integrate the information across the curriculum.

Additional resources available at the Canadian Council for Human Resources in the Environment Industry's (CCHREI's) Web site include the EnviroJob Board, the Canadian Environment Education Compendium, Environmental Labour Market Reports, links to other useful sites and much more.

Visit CCHREI's Web site, or call, to get **additional information**.

Canadian Council for Human Resources in the Environment Industry
Tel: *(403) 233-0748*
Web site: *www.cchrei.ca*

Job Futures

Written to help Canadians with their career, education and training decisions, Job Futures provides employment facts and information about today's career and education/training options as well as future trends in Canada's workplace.

This publication will be useful if you are:

- a student seeking information on the world of work and its relation to education,
- a job seeker exploring work prospects and training opportunities,
- a worker thinking about upgrading your skills or making a career change, or
- a teacher or career guidance counsellor providing advice on career or education options.

Job Futures is produced by Human Resources Development Canada (HRDC). **It is available** on the Internet, and print versions are available in public libraries and at HRDC offices. (See the Government of Canada pages of your telephone directory for the office nearest you.)

Web site: *www.hrdc-drhc.gc.ca/JobFutures*

 Job Trek: Your Generation

The pamphlet starts with an interest inventory quiz and then evolves into a game where your interests are matched to jobs that deal with information, people or things. (Cat. No. Y-152-03-94E)

For more information, contact:

Human Resources Development Canada
Public Enquiries Centre
140 Promenade du Portage
Hull, QC K1A 0J9
Fax: *(819) 953-7260*
Web site: *www.hrdc-drhc.gc.ca/career-carriere*

Labour Market Information Service

If you want to find out about job market conditions for a specific community, you'll be interested in the Labour Market Information (LMI) Service, made possible by a network of Human Resources Development Canada staff who analyze data and local events across the country.

The LMI Service provides up-to-date information ranging from employment trends for different occupations to analyses of a community's major industries. It can also give you information on what wages to expect and what services different communities offer.

LMI information is available both on paper and on the Internet. For paper products, contact your local Human Resources Development Canada office. Check the Government of Canada section of your telephone directory for the office nearest you. If you have access to the Internet, visit the LMI Web site.

Web site: *http://lmi-imt.hrdc-drhc.gc.ca*

Look Ahead, Get Ahead: Growing career opportunities for technicians and technologists

Technicians and technologists work at the frontiers of Canadian industry, where exploration and discovery are altering the way we live and work. Colleges across Canada equip technicians and technologists with the practical training and skills that prepare them for the demanding and interesting challenges of technology careers.

Published by the Canadian Technology Human Resources Board, *Look Ahead, Get Ahead* contains up-to-date information on:

- industry trends
- employment statistics
- educational requirements
- educational resources
- reference lists
- career planning information

In addition, it features profiles of 60 technicians and technologists. These profiles are real-life examples of the opportunities that abound in technology fields and how they are shaping the future. Students, teachers, career counsellors and parents will find all the information needed to make informed career decisions.

Practical and comprehensive, *Look Ahead, Get Ahead* is the ideal start to a career as a technician or technologist in Canada. **For more information**, please visit our Web site.

Web site: *www.cthrb.ca*

Looking for Work in International Development

Are you interested in world development and in working in this challenging area?

Although the number of jobs is limited, there are many possible routes to pursue, including the Canadian International Development Agency (CIDA), private companies, voluntary agencies and international organizations such as the United Nations.

Recognizing that the search for information can be confusing, CIDA has published a booklet entitled Looking for Work in International Development. This booklet describes the various types of work that exist in international development and suggests some early steps to take so that you will be considered for any openings.

This booklet is available on CIDA's Web site. **For more information, or a copy, please contact:**

Canadian International Development Agency
Public Inquiries Communications Branch
200 Promenade du Portage
Hull, QC K1A 0G4
Tel: *(819) 997-5006*
Toll-free: *1 800 230-6349*
Fax: *(819) 953-6088*
TDD/TTY: *(819) 953-5023*
         1 800 331-5018 (toll-free)
E-mail: *info@acdi-cida.gc.ca*
Web site: *www.acdi-cida.gc.ca*

Make the Skills Connection

This pamphlet shows the connection between Human Resources Development Canada's work on the Essential Skills Research Project and the Conference Board of Canada's Employability Skills. Educators, trainers, career counsellors and anyone interested in skills assessment and development will find the pamphlet useful as an introduction to:

- seeing what employers are looking for,
- linking to resources on how people use skills in different occupations, and
- describing and assessing skills.

To order, visit the Web site or contact:

Human Resources Development Canada
Public Enquiries Centre
140 Promenade du Portage
Hull, QC K1A 0J9
Fax: *(819) 953-7260*
Web site: *www.hrdc-drhc.gc.ca/career-carriere*

 **MazeMaster**

This unique career and job exploration tool for youth 16 to 29 years of age grew out of a desire to help youth in Toronto make more effective transitions from school to work and from unemployment to employment. It has been developed as a one-stop shop where youth can find relevant employment information in one place.

MazeMaster consists of six modules:

- Self-Assessment includes three interactive exercises to identify your values, skills and interests, and helps you develop an action plan.

- Labour Market Information connects you to the marketplace in Toronto by offering current information on occupational trends and employer/company profiles.

- Training and Education provides information on opportunities in Toronto by linking you to various educational institutions, programs, community agencies and information on apprenticeships.

- Self-Employment provides direction and links to resources available for starting a business, including an on-line quiz, business plan and cash flow forecast. This module also includes interviews with youth entrepreneurs.

- Job Search Techniques has interactive exercises that enable you to complete a resumé and cover letter on-line. Tips are also given on how to contact prospective employers, tap into the hidden job market and prepare for job interviews.

- Job Postings provides on-line links to newspapers, recruiters and employment agencies. It also allows employers to post jobs for youth free of charge.

MazeMaster is sponsored by the Toronto District Catholic School Board. Funding is provided by Human Resources Development Canada.

For more information, please contact:

MazeMaster Project Staff
c/o The Toronto District Catholic School Board
80 Sheppard Avenue East
Toronto, ON M2N 6E8
Tel: *(416) 222-8282* ext. 2396, 2542, 5339
Fax: *(416) 512-3428*
E-mail: *mazel@mazemaster.on.ca*
Web site: *www.mazemaster.on.ca*

Meet the Sector Councils

Sector Councils are associations that represent different parts of
the economy. Key players — such as employers, unions, professional associations and educators — work together to address the
human resource issues faced by the sector.

The councils are currently developing career awareness materials
about their sectors. **If you would like copies,** call, fax or visit their
Web sites.

Apparel Human Resource Council
Tel: *(613) 567-7495*
Fax: *(613) 567-1768*
Web site: *www.apparel-hrc.org*

Biotechnology Human Resource Council
Tel: *(613) 235-1402*
Fax: *(613) 233-7541*
Web site: *www.bhrc.ca*

Canadian Aquaculture Industry Alliance Sector Council
Tel: *(613) 239-0612*
Fax: *(613) 239-0619*
Web site: *www.aquaculture.ca*

Canadian Association of Equipment Distributors
Tel: *(613) 722-4711*
Fax: *(613) 722-0099*
Web site: *www.caed.org*

Canadian Automotive Repair and Service Council
Tel: *(905) 709-1010*
Fax: *(905) 709-1013*
Web site: *www.cars-council.ca*

Canadian Aviation Maintenance Council
Tel: *(613) 727-8272*
Fax: *(613) 727-7018*
Web site: *www.camc.ca*

Canadian Council for Human Resources in the Environment Industry
Tel: *(403) 233-0748*
Fax: *(403) 269-9544*
Web site: *www.cchrei.ca*

Canadian Council of Professional Engineers
Tel: *(613) 232-2474*
Fax: *(613) 230-5759*
Web site: *www.ccpe.ca/*

Canadian Council of Professional Fish Harvesters
Tel: *(613) 235-3474*
Fax: *(613) 231-4313*
Web site: *www.ccpfh-ccpp.org*

Canadian Grocery Producers Council
Tel: *(905) 670-3844*
Fax: *(905) 670-3855*

Canadian Professional Logistics Institute
Tel: *(416) 363-3005*
Fax: *(416) 363-5598*
Web site: *www.loginstitute.ca*

Canadian Steel Trade and Employment Congress
Tel: *(416) 480-1797*
Fax: *(416) 480-2986*
Web site: *www.cstec.ca*

Canadian Technology Human Resources Board
Tel: *(613) 233-1955*
Toll-free: *1 800 216-9462*
Web site: *www.cthrb.ca*

Canadian Tourism Human Resource Council
Tel: *(613) 231-6949*
Fax: *(613) 231-6853*
Web site: *www.cthrc.ca*

Canadian Trucking Human Resources Council
Tel: *(613) 244-4800*
Fax: *(613) 244-4535*
Web site: *www.cthrc.com*

Cultural Human Resources Council
Tel: *(613) 562-1535*
Fax: *(613) 562-2982*
Web site: *www.culturalhrc.ca*

Electronic and Appliance Service Industry
Tel: *(416) 241-3550*
Toll-free: *1 800 405-1586*
Fax: *(416) 241-1137*
Web site: *www.easi.ca/easi*

Forum for International Trade Training
Tel: *(613) 230-3553*
Fax: *(613) 230-6808*
Web site: *www.fitt.ca*

Horticultural Human Resource Council
Tel: *(506) 363-3310*
Fax: *(506) 363-8991*

Mining Industry Training and Adjustment Council
Tel: *(613) 230-1413*
Fax: *(613) 230-0603*
Web site: *www.mitac.ca*

National Seafood Sector Council
Tel: *(613) 782-2391*
Fax: *(613) 782-2386*
Web site: *www.nssc.ca*

Retail Council of Canada
Tel: *1 888 373-8245* (toll-free)
Fax: *(416) 922-8011*
Web site: *www.retailcouncil.org*

Sectoral Skills Council of the Electrical and Electronic
Manufacturing Industry
Tel: *(613) 567-3036*
Fax: *(613) 567-3195*

Software Human Resource Council
Tel: *(613) 237-8551*
Fax: *(613) 230-3490*
Web site: *www.shrc.ca*

Textiles Human Resources Council
Tel: *(613) 230-7217*
Fax: *(613) 230-1270*
Web site: *www3.sympatico.ca/thrc*

The Packaging Careers Council of Canada
Fax: *(416) 490-7844*
Web site: *www.packagingcareers.org*

WITT (Women in Trades and Technology) National Network
Tel: *(613) 546-8558*
Fax: *(613) 541-0734*
Web site: *www.wittnn.com*

In addition to career information, many of the Sector
Councils are also developing job-search tools and sponsoring
youth internships. Check out the *Job-Search Tools* and
Work Experience Opportunities sections of this publication
or check the *Index by Organization and Program Listing* to see
whether the Sector Council you're interested in has a
listing elsewhere in this publication.

Minding Your Own Business

Is entrepreneurship or starting a small business a realistic career option for you? This booklet will help you determine whether you have the right qualities and skills to succeed in a small business. Information and advice about starting a small business are also provided — including information on the different approaches to a business start-up. (Cat. No. LM-356-12-94)

For copies, contact:

Human Resources Development Canada
Public Enquiries Centre
140 Promenade du Portage
Hull, QC K1A 0J9
Fax: *(819) 953-7260*
Web site: *www.hrdc-drhc.gc.ca/career-carriere*

REALM: Creating Work You Want

REALM is the first national career and entrepreneurship magazine and webzine targeting Canadians 18 to 29 years of age. Created by, for and about youth, REALM (and its French counterpart SPHÉRE: Le monde du travail recrée) is also the first national magazine to address the concerns of young people making their way through today's revolutionized economy.

A cost is associated. **For more information, or to order, contact:**

Yes Canada-BC Publishing
Tel: *(604) 412-4134*
Toll-free: *1 877 REALM-99*
Fax: *(604) 412-4144*
E-mail: *lisa@realm.net*
Web site: *http://realm.net*

🔆 School – Your Track to Job Skills

This colourful pamphlet, which can also be used as a poster, illustrates how school subjects give students working skills they can add to their resumés. (Cat. No. Y-153-03-94)

For copies, contact:

Human Resources Development Canada
Public Enquiries Centre
140 Promenade du Portage
Hull, QC K1A 0J9
Fax: *(819) 953-7260*
Web site: *www.hrdc-drhc.gc.ca/career-carriere*

🔆 Software Career Discovery Centre

The Software Career Discovery Centre provides Canadian high-school students with the tools they need to make informed career choices in the dynamic field of software. DiscoverIT.org includes information for students, educators and parents on:

- career planning tools;
- labour market trends, including salary ranges;
- comprehensive job profiles based on the Occupational Skills Profile Model — a new industry standard;
- centralized information on post-secondary educational institutions and financing options;
- classroom and self-directed learning activities to help educators and students expand their educational horizons;
- educator resources, including a venue for sharing excellence; and
- links to key sites and partners.

For information, contact:

Software Human Resource Council
30 Metcalfe Street, Suite 400
Ottawa, ON K1P 5L4
Tel: *(613) 237-8551*
Fax: *(613) 230-3490*
E-mail: *info@shrc.ca*
Web site: *www.discoverIT.org*

🌟 Space Education and Awareness Program

The science and technology sector is one of Canada's major areas of growth at the dawn of the new millennium. The Canadian Space Agency's (CSA's) Space Education and Awareness Program uses the unique appeal of space to turn Canada's youth on to the exciting challenges and rewards of scientific studies.

Resource Materials

The Space Education and Awareness Program produces resource materials such as posters, booklets, videos and Web sites highlighting the science and mathematics behind such fascinating subjects as space missions, microgravity, robotics and Earth observation. Information on Canada's role in the development of the International Space Station, CSA's astronaut training, Canadian achievements in space exploration and more are made available through brochures and different documentation. See our Web site for information on the many new initiatives.

Canadian Space Resource Centres

The CSA's network of five Canadian Space Resource Centres (CSRCs) provides students, teachers and the general public with ready access to a wide range of information about space. The CRSCs distribute printed and audiovisual information and curriculum support materials free of charge or for a nominal fee based on cost-recovery. These materials include information on astronomy, human space flight, space and life sciences, and many other topics.

Grants and Contributions Program

The Grants and Contributions Program has been established to help finance space-related activities — from promoting the Canadian Space Program to developing educational resources — and to provide support for groups, associations, space camps, etc. Submissions are accepted several times throughout the year, and application forms are available through the CSA.

For more information, contact:

Canadian Space Agency
Tel: *(450) 926-4349*
Toll-free: *1 800 511-3500* (CSRCs only)
Fax: *(450) 926-4352*
Web site: *www.space.gc.ca/kidspace/index.html*

❂ The Directory of Canadian Universities

The Directory of Canadian Universities is the only official guide to Canadian universities. Ideal for guidance counsellors, librarians, high-school students, career counsellors and teachers, this directory provides the most current information on Canadian universities in a reliable, easy-to-use, one-volume format. Compiled, updated and verified annually, it is the most authoritative directory of its kind, and includes detailed information on admission requirements, programs, grading and credit systems, fees, housing, facilities, and enrolment.

A key feature is the National Program Index, a definitive listing of over 10 000 undergraduate and graduate programs. Available for $45 in Canada, **the directory can be ordered on-line or by contacting:**

Association of Universities and Colleges of Canada
350 Albert Street
Ottawa, ON K1R 1B1
Tel: *(613) 563-1236*
Fax: *(613) 563-9745*
E-mail: *publications@aucc.ca*
Web site: *www.aucc.ca*

 The Edge

The Edge is a unique resource that encourages teens to think about their future and about the importance of getting an education. It contains articles on career development as well as self-directed exercises designed to help teens develop a better understanding of themselves and the world of work. (Cat. No. Y-109-02-94E)

For copies, visit the Web site or contact:

National Life/Work Centre
Tel: *1 888 533-5683* (toll-free)
E-mail: *lifework@nbnet.nb.ca*
Web site: *http://lifework.ca*

 The Real Game Series

The Real Game Series is a unique, interactive and experiential career education program that enables students to experience the realities of the adult world in a fun and stimulating way and to understand how choices and decisions made now may affect the quality of their lives as adults. The individual games in the series include:

- The Play Real Game — kindergarten to grade 4
- The Make It Real Game — grades 5 to 6
- The Real Game — grades 7 and 8
- The Be Real Game — grades 9 and 10
- The Get Real Game — grades 11 and 12
- The Real Times/Real Life Game — adult

Each product is developed to operate effectively in the absence of any other program in the series. Although they have strong common elements, particularly in terms of their experiential and role-playing frame of reference and their setting in participants' futures, each program is unique. Every game provides a personal career-building context that participants and facilitators at all levels find enjoyable and stimulating.

A cost is associated. **For more information, or to order, contact:**

National Life/Work Centre
Memramcook Institute
PO Box 180
Saint-Joseph, NB E0A 2Y0
Tel: *1 888 533-5683* or *1 800 956-4263* (toll-free)
Fax: *(506) 758-0353*
E-mail: *lifework@nbnet.nb.ca*
Web site: *www.realgame.ca*

The Work Handbook

This handbook will be useful to you if you are thinking about
or actually facing career changes that will affect you and your
family. It contains general information about resources — people,
organizations, skills and the Internet — that can give you a head
start on managing career change.

For more information, contact:

Canada Career Consortium
1204 – 66 Slater Street
Ottawa, ON K1P 5H1
Fax: *(613) 230-7681*
Web site: *www.careerccc.org*

Volunteering Works!

Volunteering is a great way to learn new skills and give back to
your community. Volunteering Works! is a suite of career awareness
products that can help demonstrate the link between volunteering
activities and paid work experience as well as the overall
importance of volunteerism in the community.

There are five products in this suite:

- Volunteering Works! Be part of shaping your future — Designed for youth aged 15 to 30, this fun booklet is packed full of information and activities. It answers some important questions about volunteering, offers advice on getting started and opens doors to the world of paid work.
- Volunteering Works! Facilitator's Guide — This goes hand-in-hand with the youth booklet and is designed for use by teachers, counsellors and managers of volunteer programs. Detailed activity and resource sections assist facilitators in helping youth get started in a volunteer program or activity.

- Volunteering Works! Parents Guide — This booklet introduces parents to the world of youth volunteering. Concise and easy-to-read, the guide addresses some important issues facing the voluntary sector today and offers advice on being an active part of your child's volunteer experience.

- Volunteering Works! promotional posters — These posters will stop traffic in school halls and drop-in centres and all over your community. Raise awareness about the importance of the volunteer experience as a way to develop valuable workplace skills and gain experience.

- Volunteering Works! Web site — This fun and interactive Web site has something for everyone. Youth can explore skills development opportunities made possible through volunteering. Parents can link to career information and volunteering sites. Teachers and facilitators can download exercises and lesson plans.

For more information about Volunteering Works!, please contact:

Volunteer Canada
430 Gilmour Street
Ottawa, ON K2P 0R8
Tel: *1 800 670-0401* (toll-free)
Fax: *(613) 231-6725*
E-mail: *volunteer.canada@sympatico.ca*
Web site: *www.volunteer.ca*

⚡ What's your favourite subject?

Targeting high-school students, these five pamphlets highlight the link between school subjects, skills learned and occupational opportunities. They also examine the educational levels required for entry into various occupations as well as recommended high-school courses as preparation.

For more information, contact:

Human Resources Development Canada
Public Enquiries Centre
140 Promenade du Portage
Hull, QC K1A 0J9
Fax: *(819) 953-7260*
Web site: *www.hrdc-drhc.gc.ca/career-carriere*

⚡ Youth Info Fairs

Youth Info Fairs, held in towns and cities across the country as part of Canada's Youth Employment Strategy, target youth aged 15 to 30. Young Canadians will find it worthwhile to visit one of these fairs and get easily accessible information on the programs and services offered by the Government of Canada.

Staff at the booths help participating youth by identifying a wide variety of useful resources and handing out plenty of brochures and helpful hints. Some Youth Info Fairs also provide workshops on job-search techniques and career planning.

Is a Youth Info Fair coming to your area? **To find out**, call the toll-free Youth Info Line or visit the Youth Employment Strategy Web site.

Youth Info Line: *1 800 935-5555*
Web site: *www.youth.gc.ca/YES*

Educational and Other Assistance

Canada Education Savings Grant

The Canada Education Savings Grant provides 20% on any amount up to $2000 saved in a family's Registered Education Savings Plan (RESP) — to a maximum of $400 a year per child — to encourage families to save for post-secondary education costs. This will help offset the need for student loans, and reduce or eliminate student debt on graduation.

The investment income earned on the savings and the Government of Canada grant payments to the RESP are sheltered from tax until the student uses the money to finance the cost of post-secondary education.

RESPs are flexible and can be moved between siblings. If the student does not pursue higher education within a reasonable period of time after high school, the grant portion would have to be repaid.

For more information, please contact:

Tel: *1 888 276-3624* (toll-free)
Web site: *www.hrdc-drhc.gc.ca/cesg*

Thinking of starting your own business?
Check out the *Entrepreneurship* section of this
publication for information about the financial and
practical assistance available to young
entrepreneurs across Canada.

Canada Pension Plan

The Canada Pension Plan (CPP) provides basic benefits when a person with sufficient CPP contributions becomes disabled, retires or dies. The CPP also provides benefits to the children of disabled or deceased contributors.

For you to be eligible for one or both of the following benefits, your parent or parents must have made sufficient contributions to the CPP, and they must be receiving a CPP disability benefit and/or be deceased. Also, if you are between the ages of 18 and 25, you must be attending school full-time at a recognized institution.

The Disabled Contributor's Child's Benefit is a monthly benefit paid to a natural or adopted child, or to a child who is in the care and control of a CPP disability pensioner.

The Surviving Child's Benefit is paid to a natural or adopted child, or to a child who was in the care and control of a deceased CPP contributor at the time of death.

For further information, contact a Human Resources Development Canada office or visit our Web site.

Tel: *1 800 277-9914* (toll-free)
TTY: *1 800 255-4786* (toll-free)
Web site: *www.hrdc-drhc.gc.ca/isp/*

Canada's Northern Scientific Training Program

Funds to help support students specializing in northern scientific studies are available to Canadian universities with an officially recognized institute or committee for northern studies.

Priority is given to graduate students. However, senior undergraduate students entering their final year and intending to undertake an honour's thesis based on northern fieldwork or research that will be continued in subsequent graduate studies are also eligible. Post-doctoral students are not supported.

The program helps students pay for transportation and living costs while obtaining practical fieldwork experience in Canada's North, developing interest and expertise in northern issues, and improving research skills.

You are eligible if you are a Canadian citizen or permanent resident enrolled in a Canadian university and are interested in northern studies with field experience in Canada's North.

For more information, please contact:

Department of Indian Affairs and Northern Development
Northern Scientific Training Program
10 Wellington Street
Hull, QC K1A 0H4
Tel: *(819) 997-9667*
Fax: *(819) 994-6419*
E-mail: *nstp@inac.gc.ca*
Web site: *www.inac.gc.ca/pubs/northern/nstp.html*

Canada Student Loans Program

This program provides financial assistance for needy full-time and part-time students attending post-secondary educational institutions. The 1998 Budget introduced a range of new measures to help student borrowers reduce and better manage debt:

- Low-income student borrowers with dependants are eligible for a Canada Study Grant up to $3120 per year for full-time students and up to $1920 for part-time students.

- More borrowers in financial difficulty are able to benefit from Interest Relief as a result of a 9% increase to the income threshold for eligibility. *

- Up to 30 months of Interest Relief over the life of the loan is now available. *

- Borrowers experiencing serious financial hardship may be eligible for a reduction of the principal amount of their loan. *

- New measures to enhance communications with students and strengthen student and institutional eligibility will continue to improve the overall performance and accountability of the Canada Student Loans Program. They will also help to reduce the risk of student loan defaults and bankruptcies in the future.

Application forms are available from financial aid offices at colleges and universities, and from student aid offices in the provincial/ territorial ministries of education. Apply early!

For more information (but not application forms), contact:

Canada Student Loans Program
Human Resources Development Canada
Hull, QC K1A 0M5
Tel: *(819) 994-1844*
Web site: *www.hrdc-drhc.gc.ca/student_loans/*

* See your bank, credit union or caisse populaire for details.

Community Volunteer Income Tax Program

This community-based outreach program helps people with straightforward tax situations complete their income tax returns free of charge. It is designed to help the people who need it most: newcomers to Canada, low-income wage earners, students and seniors.

To serve your community by volunteering to help people with their tax returns, or to get help yourself, call Canada Customs and Revenue Agency's (CCRA's) toll-free number and ask for the Community Volunteer Income Tax Coordinator. You can also visit the CCRA Web site **for more information**.

Community Volunteer Income Tax Coordinator
Canada Customs and Revenue Agency
Toll-free: *1 800 959-8281*
Web site: *www.ccra-adrc.gc.ca/tax/individuals/volunteer/index-e.html*

Employment Insurance

In most instances, if you worked at least 420 to 700 hours in the last 52 weeks at a job where Employment Insurance contributions were taken off your paycheque and you are now unemployed, you may be eligible for Employment Insurance benefits.

While you look for work, Employment Insurance benefits pay 55% of your average insurable earnings, which are calculated from your last 26 weeks worked. If you earned less than $25 921 and if you or your spouse support a dependant, you can receive a maximum of 75% of your average insurable earnings.

The program pays maternity, parental and sickness benefits. Changes will be put in place by January 2001 to extend parental benefits up to one year. Adjustment benefits such as training, work sharing and job creation are also part of the Employment Insurance program.

Those who quit work without just cause or are fired for misconduct are not eligible for Employment Insurance until they again qualify through new employment.

For more information, contact your nearest Government of Canada Employment Insurance office listed under Human Resources Development Canada in the Government of Canada pages of your telephone directory.

Post–Secondary Student Support Program

This program provides assistance toward the cost of a post-secondary education.

It is available to registered First Nations and Inuit youths who have been accepted by an accredited post-secondary educational institution and have been residents of Canada for 12 consecutive months. However, the program is not available to persons who are eligible for support under special arrangements for post-secondary support — such as the James Bay and Northern Quebec Agreement or the Northwest Territories Student Financing Assistance Program.

Deadlines are determined by First Nations education authorities and the regional offices of the Department of Indian Affairs and Northern Development (DIAND).

For more information, and to apply, please contact your band council or the nearest DIAND office.

Student Need Assessment Software

This Windows-compatible software gives you an idea of the potential value of your Canada Student Loan. To calculate this amount, you input your expenses (e.g., books, tuition, living expenses) and sources of income (e.g., parental contributions, savings, earnings from summer or part-time jobs).

The program will take you about 15 to 20 minutes to complete, and it refers to potential funding from the Canada Student Loans Program only. For information on estimating provincial student loan funding, contact your provincial or territorial student assistance office.

To access the need assessment software on the Internet, visit one of the two Human Resources Development Canada Web sites.

Web site: *http://205.207.175.25/cgi-bin/hrdcsnas/snasen.html*
www.canlearn.ca/english/fin/debtfreeguide/csl/hrdcsnas/snasen.shtml

Students and Income Tax

Information on entitlements and other items of interest to working students is available in Canada Customs and Revenue Agency's (CCRA's) income tax guides and in a pamphlet entitled Students and Income Tax. You can find out about:

- claiming and transferring education amounts and tuition fees,
- claiming the goods and services/harmonized sales tax (GST/HST) credit,
- claiming interest paid on student loans, and
- claiming moving expenses.

The guides and pamphlet are available from any tax services office. (The addresses and telephone numbers of the offices are listed in the Government of Canada section of your telephone directory.) These publications are also available on CCRA's Web site. You can also visit CCRA's tax information for students Web site.

Canada Customs and Revenue Agency
Web site: *www.ccra-adrc.gc.ca*
        www.ccra-adrc.gc.ca/menu/EmenuGNN.html
        (tax information for students)

Entrepreneurship

Aboriginal Business Canada

Aboriginal Business Canada works with Aboriginal entrepreneurs to promote the development, competitiveness and success of Aboriginal business in Canadian and world markets.

One of the program's strategic priorities is youth entrepreneurship. Aboriginal Business Canada provides services and financial support to Canadian status and non-status Indians, Inuit and Métis between the ages of 18 and 29. Assistance to youth-owned businesses includes business advisory services as well as support related to developing business plans, marketing and financing the start-up operation, and acquiring, expanding or modernizing a commercially viable business.

A separate initiative, the Aboriginal Youth Business Initiative, pro-vides lending services and business support to young Aboriginal entrepreneurs. These funds are administered by Aboriginal financial organizations. This initiative also supports a wide variety of entre-preneurship promotion activities, including mentoring programs and workshops on entrepreneurship.

For more information, contact the Aboriginal Business Canada office nearest you or visit the Web site.

Web site: *http://abc.gc.ca*

Edmonton:	*(780) 495-2954*
Halifax:	*(902) 426-2018*
Montréal:	*(514) 283-1828*
Ottawa:	*(613) 954-4064*
Saskatoon:	*(306) 975-4329*
Toronto:	*(416) 973-8800*
Vancouver:	*(604) 666-3871*
Winnipeg:	*(204) 983-7316*

ACOA Seed Capital and Counselling Program

This program offers loans of up to $15 000 for business start-up or expansion, and covers up to $2000 for business counselling and training costs. Applicants must be between 18 and 29 years of age and living in Atlantic Canada.

For more information, call the Atlantic Canada Opportunities Agency (ACOA) toll-free number.

Tel: *1 800 668-1010*

Business Development Bank of Canada

The Business Development Bank of Canada (BDC) offers a complete range of services, particularly financial and consulting services, to help small Canadian businesses grow.

BDC's vast range of consulting services is designed to meet the needs of entrepreneurs at every stage of business development. The Bank also has programs specially designed to meet the needs of high-technology or knowledge-based businesses, exporters, Aboriginal enterprises and emerging markets.

For more information, contact the BDC branch nearest you, call the toll-free number or visit the Bank's Web site.

Tel: *1 888 INFO-BDC (1 888 463-6232)*
Web site: *www.bdc.ca*

> If you have a small export business in Western Canada and need employees to help implement your marketing strategy, take a look at the International Trade Personnel Program described in the *Work Experience Opportunities* section of this publication.

Canadian Foundation for Economic Education

The Foundation has a number of print, video and CD-ROM resources available to support economics and entrepreneurship education.

Entrepreneurship for Canadians: The Spirit of Adventure

Designed for students at the high-school, community college and university level, this series focuses on the formative stages of entrepreneurship education. Six half-hour programs are presented on two video cassettes (VHS format). An orientation video and user's guide are also included.

Planning for Success

This interactive CD-ROM, produced for the Canadian Bankers Association, is designed to support students of entrepreneurship as well as beginning and experienced entrepreneurs.

The Spirit Lives: Aboriginal Entrepreneurs in Canada

These six half-hour video programs and the accompanying user's guide are designed to assist Aboriginal teachers, trainers and economic development officers in the delivery of entrepreneurship instruction. This series features Aboriginal entrepreneurs from across Canada.

For more information on these and other resources, contact:

Canadian Foundation for Economic Education
2 St. Clair Avenue West, Suite 501
Toronto, ON M4V 1L5
Tel: *(416) 968-2236*
Fax: *(416) 968-0488*
E-mail: *mail@cfee.org*
Web site: *www.cfee.org*

CED/CFDC Youth Strategy

To reduce the number of youths who leave rural Quebec in favour of large urban centres, Canada Economic Development for Quebec Regions has set up a program of assistance for young local entrepreneurs. To be eligible, they must:

- be between 18 and 35 years of age, and
- reside within the territory of one of the 54 Community Futures Development Corporations (CFDC) throughout Quebec.

Loans of up to $15 000 may be used to purchase, start up, modernize or expand a business.

The young entrepreneurs receive customized support and are closely monitored for the duration of the loan. Financial support can be offered to two young entrepreneurs working on the same project.

For more information, please contact:

Canada Economic Development for Quebec Regions
Tour de la Bourse
800 Victoria Square, Suite 3800
PO Box 247
Montréal, QC H4K 1E8
Tel: *(514) 496-4636*
Toll-free: *1 800 322-4636*
Web site: *www.dec-ced.gc.ca*

Community Futures Development Corporations
979 de Bourgogne Street, Suite 530
Sainte-Foy, QC G1W 2L4
Tel: *(418) 658-1530*
Web site: *www.reseau-sadc.qc.ca*

Contact! The Canadian Management Network

Contact! The Canadian Management Network provides several unique resources for youth business:

- the most complete directory of over 2800 Canadian small-business support organizations
- profiles of multicultural advisors — who advise on foreign business cultures and practices
- all of Canada's major business awards described with nomination information included
- Your Guide to Government of Canada Services and Support for Small Business
- Right from Home: Starting a Home-Based Business — a 100-page how-to guide by two leading authors
- over 650 on-line how-to publications, complete and free of charge to download
- Coffee Break Listserv — a discussion and networking centre that will help you network with other business associates
- descriptions of over 300 business management software tools, with contact information

For more information, please contact:

Industry Canada
Entrepreneurship and Small Business Office
235 Queen Street
Ottawa, ON K1A 0H5
Web site: *http://strategis.ic.gc.ca/contact*

Export Assistance

Canada Economic Development for Quebec Regions is a federal agency that helps young Quebec entrepreneurs link up with the network known as Team Canada. This network contains most export assistance agencies in the federal government, and it benefits from the expertise of 600 trade commissioners and representatives around the world. The network provides information, advisory services and access to other key players in the export sector.

Through its IDEA-SME Program, the Agency offers small- and medium-sized businesses financial support in the form of repayable contributions of up to 50% of eligible costs.

Areas eligible for financial assistance include:

- marketing strategies;
- projects providing support to new exporters; and
- activities complementing foreign market development programs (e.g., production of promotional material aimed at international markets).

For more information, please contact:

Canada Economic Development for Quebec Regions
Tour de la Bourse
800 Victoria Square, Suite 3800
PO Box 247
Montréal, QC H4K 1E8
Tel: *(514) 496-4636*
Toll-free: *1 800 322-4636*
Web site: *www.dec-ced.gc.ca*

🌢 Export Development Corporation

No company is too small to export, and no exporter is too small for the Export Development Corporation (EDC). That's why we have specialized services for smaller exporters. From the application process to credit approvals on foreign buyers to filing claims — our services are fast and efficient.

Through a toll-free hotline, our Emerging Exporters Team delivers accounts receivable insurance to firms with annual export sales up to $1 million.

Here's what to expect when you call the hotline:

- answers to questions about how EDC can help small business succeed internationally,
- a specialist who will take your insurance or loan application over the phone,
- more information about EDC's smaller exporter financial solutions, and
- referral to other sources of export assistance.

The hotline is available Monday to Friday, 9 a.m. to 5 p.m., across Canada.

For more information, contact:

Export Development Corporation
151 O'Connor Street
Ottawa, ON K1A 1K3
Hotline: *1 800 850-9626*
Fax: *(613) 598-6871*
Web site: *www.edc.ca*

First Jobs in Science and Technology

The First Jobs in Science and Technology program provides small businesses with funding to hire recent science and technology graduates. The program enables small businesses to gain valuable technological expertise while offering youth in Western Canada their first jobs in areas related to their field of training and their chosen careers.

The First Jobs program will provide up to $37 500 in salary support over a three-year period.

For more information, please contact:

Western Economic Diversification Canada
Toll-free: *1 888 338-WEST (9378)*
Web site: *www.wd.gc.ca*

First Nations and Inuit Youth Business Program

The First Nations and Inuit Youth Business Program promotes youth access to seed capital and mentoring. Under the present agreement, the National Aboriginal Capital Corporations Association manages the program. It ensures national delivery of this program in both official languages through its network of member corporations.

This program will enable Aboriginal lending institutions to offer the following to First Nations and Inuit youth living on-reserve in recognized communities:

- proactive business opportunity advice and counselling,
- mentoring and advisory support, and
- seed capital to explore or develop a business opportunity.

Out-of-school, unemployed First Nations youth who are between 15 and 30 years of age are eligible. Underemployed youth, part-time students and those at risk of dropping out of school are also considered for this program.

For more information, contact the nearest Department of Indian Affairs and Northern Development (DIAND) office, or call your local Aboriginal Capital Corporation. Information is available on the DIAND Web site and the Aboriginal Youth Network Web site.

Web site: *www.inac.gc.ca/youth/index.html* (DIAND)
www.ayn.ca (Aboriginal Youth Network)

 # FITTskills

Set your sights on the world of international trade and global business — and we'll give you the skills, knowledge and confidence for success.

The Forum for International Trade Training (FITT) is a Sector Council established by Human Resources Development Canada (HRDC), and working in partnership with HRDC, the Department of Foreign Affairs and International Trade, Industry Canada, and Agriculture and Agri-Food Canada. We're Canada's centre for international trade training, and our FITTskills program provides a hands-on, comprehensive training package focusing on the practical aspects of international business.

FITTskills consists of eight modules:

- Global Entrepreneurship
- International Marketing
- International Trade Finance
- International Trade Logistics
- International Market Entry and Distribution
- International Trade Research

- Legal Aspects of International Trade
- International Trade Management

Completion of the FITTskills program leads to a diploma in international trade and fulfills the educational requirement for the professional designation of Certified International Trade Professional (CITP).

FITTskills is available via the Internet and through community colleges, universities and private organizations across Canada.

For more information, contact FITT at:

30 Metcalfe Street, 4th Floor
Ottawa, ON K1P 5L4
Tel: *(613) 230-3553*
Toll-free: *1 800 561-3488*
Fax: *(613) 230-6808*
E-mail: *corp@fitt.ca*
Web site: *www.fitt.ca*

 **IDEA-SME**

Offered through Canada Economic Development for Quebec Regions, IDEA-SME provides a range of information and consulting services to small- and medium-sized enterprises (SMEs) in Quebec.

It also provides services and funds activities in such areas as:

- innovation, research and development, and design;
- development of markets;
- export; and
- assistance to entrepreneurship and development of the business climate.

Eligible projects include:

- consultant studies;
- implementation of a marketing plan;
- organization of fairs, conferences and seminars; and
- entrepreneurship competitions and scholarships for excellence.

For more information, please contact:

Canada Economic Development for Quebec Regions
Tour de la Bourse
800 Victoria Square, Suite 3800
PO Box 247
Montréal, QC H4K 1E8
Tel: *(514) 496-4636*
Toll-free: *1 800 322-4636*
Web site: *www.dec-ced.gc.ca*

Selling to Government

If you are interested in providing goods and/or services to the Government of Canada, call the Contracts Canada Information Centre, the toll-free number, or the nearest Public Works and Government Services Canada (PWGSC) regional office.

Contracts Canada Information Centre
Tel: *(819) 956-3440*
Toll-free: *1 800 811-1148*
Web site: *http://contractscanada.gc.ca*

PWGSC Regional Offices

Dartmouth:	*(902) 496-5433*
Edmonton:	*(780) 497-3635*
Mississauga:	*(905) 795-5222*
Moncton:	*(506) 851-2307*
Montréal:	*(514) 496-3339* or *(514) 496-3390*
Québec:	*(418) 649-2871* or *(418) 649-2872*
Regina:	*(306) 780-7390*
St John's:	*(709) 772-2618*
Vancouver:	*(604) 666-1098*
Victoria:	*(250) 363-3264*
Winnipeg:	*(204) 983-8226*

Student Business Loans

With the help of Student Business Loans, young people with business ideas and entrepreneurial drive can develop their own summer jobs. Students living in Newfoundland, Quebec, Manitoba, Saskatchewan, Alberta, British Columbia, Yukon, the Northwest Territories or Nunavut and intending to return to school full-time in the fall are eligible for loans of up to $3000 to help them start up and run their own small businesses during the summer months. The program is a part of the Student Summer Job Action component of Canada's Youth Employment Strategy.

These loans are interest-free until early October, when full payment is due. Students who repay their loans in full (having a value of $1000 or more) between the beginning of August and the beginning of September will be eligible for a cash rebate of $100.

For more information about the program, call the Business Development Bank of Canada (BDC) or visit the BDC Web site. You can also contact your local Human Resources Development Canada (HRDC) office or HRDC Office for Students. These are both listed in the Government of Canada pages of your telephone directory.

Business Development Bank of Canada
Tel: *1 888 463-6232* (toll-free)
Web site: *www.bdc.ca*

Western Youth Entrepreneurs Program

The Western Youth Entrepreneurs Program helps young people between 18 and 29 years of age recognize their entrepreneurial goals and start a small business. The program offers mentoring and counselling as well as guidance in:

- business planning,
- development and operations, and
- accessing small-business loans of up to $25 000.

Applications can be made at any of the 100 offices of the Community Futures Development Corporations located throughout Western Canada.

For more information, please contact:

Western Economic Diversification Canada
Toll-free: *1 888 338-WEST (9378)*
Web site: *www.wd.gc.ca*

 **You Corp.**

The You Corp. kiosk travels to high schools, colleges and university campuses for one-day events such as career fairs or information sessions promoting entrepreneurship as a career choice. At each venue, the kiosk features a successful young entrepreneur and a bilingual facilitator who will answer questions about the various programs and initiatives in place for young people who want to start a business.

A brochure entitled "entrepreneurship: reality check" is also available for youth who are thinking about starting and operating their own businesses.

For more information, visit the Web site or contact:

You Corp.
Tel: *1 800 567-2345* (toll-free)
Web site: *www.you-corp.com*

 **Young Entrepreneur Financing Program**

The Young Entrepreneur Financing Program gives start-up entrepreneurs between the ages of 18 and 34 a solid foundation for building a new business. The Business Development Bank of Canada (BDC) offers term financing of up to $25 000 as well as 50 hours of tailor-made business management support to help ensure that entrepreneurs with commercially viable business proposals and excellent potential get their businesses off the ground.

For more information, contact the BDC branch nearest you, call the toll-free number or visit the Bank's Web site.

Tel: *1 888 INFO-BDC* (*1 888 463-6232*)
Web site: www.bdc.ca

 **Young Entrepreneurs Awards**

Every year, the Business Development Bank of Canada (BDC) presents awards to outstanding young Canadian entrepreneurs representing each province and territory. The winners are chosen by a panel of judges made up of local business people, members of boards of trade and chambers of commerce, business professionals, and representatives from BDC.

Winners receive substantial help with the growth of their business by being matched with a business leader in a year-long mentorship program. Mentors act as guides and knowledgeable counsellors, helping young entrepreneurs broaden the scope of their business acumen and network of contacts.

Judges look for, among other criteria, innovative entrepreneurs with operating success, exporting potential and involvement with the new economy. Young entrepreneurs can nominate themselves or be nominated by others.

Application forms can be obtained at any BDC branch, by calling BDC's toll-free number or by visiting BDC's Web site.

Tel: *1 888 INFO-BDC (1 888 463-6232)*
Web site: *www.bdc.ca*

Your Guide to Government of Canada Services and Support for Small Business

Industry Canada's Your Guide to Government of Canada Services and Support for Small Business provides basic information — and gives contact points for obtaining more details — on everything from getting started to accessing new markets.

The guide is available through Canada Business Service Centres and selected branches of the Business Development Bank of Canada as well as on Industry Canada's Strategis Web site.

Web site: *http://strategis.ic.gc.ca*

Youth Ventures Program – Newfoundland

This program develops entrepreneurial skills in youth by supporting summer enterprises initiated by students. It is sponsored by the Newfoundland and Labrador Association of Business Development Centres with funding from the Canada/Newfoundland Agreement on Economic Renewal and the Atlantic Canada Opportunities Agency.

Students returning to high school or post-secondary institutions are eligible.

For more information, please contact:

Atlantic Canada Opportunities Agency
The John Cabot Building
10 Barter's Hill, 11th Floor
PO Box 1060, Station C
St. John's, NF A1C 5M5
Tel: *(709) 772-0212*
Fax: *(709) 772-2712*

Youth Ventures Program
175 Airport Boulevard
Gander, NF A1V 1W5
Tel: *(709) 651-4060*
Fax: *(709) 651-3295*

Job-Search Tools

Applying for Your Social Insurance Number

Everyone should have a social insurance number (SIN). The SIN is a nine-digit number by which the Canadian government identifies individuals for the purposes of taxation, Employment Insurance and pensions. The SIN is important, particularly if you are applying for a job or if you are registering at a university or college.

To apply for a SIN, you must complete an application form and provide an original or true certified copy of two documents that prove your identity and status in Canada. Application forms may be picked up at your local Human Resources Development Canada (HRDC) office. Check the Government of Canada section of your telephone directory for the office nearest you.

HRDC encourages you to apply for your SIN in person at an HRDC office. This process is faster and more convenient, as it does not require you to part with your valuable identity documents or pay for getting photocopies of documents notarized. You may also apply by mail. There is no fee for an initial application for a SIN card.

To find out what types of documents are needed in your particular case, contact your local HRDC office or visit the SIN Web site at *www.hrdc-drhc.gc.ca/nas/nas2120e.shtml*. To apply by mail, send your completed application form and identity documents to:

Social Insurance Registration
PO Box 7000
Bathhurst, NB E2A 4T1

Your documents will be returned to you with your SIN card.

Apply to Teach Network: Career Opportunities in the Education Sector

The Apply to Teach Network (ATTN) is Canada's largest on-line teacher recruitment database. It connects teachers directly to hiring school boards and private employers. A partnership among Industry Canada's SkillNet.ca, Innovations Media, and the Centre for Education and Training, ATTN serves the needs of teachers and the academic recruiting community.

For more information, visit the Web site or contact:

Centre for Education and Training
Tel: *(905) 949-9900* ext. 2391
Fax: *(905) 949-6004*
E-mail: *amalik@tcet.com*
Web site: *www.attn.org* or
www.skillnet.ca

Campus WorkLink

Campus WorkLink is a comprehensive career database and employment resource specially designed for university and college students, recent graduates, and the employers seeking to hire them. Job seekers can access a variety of resources to help them find the careers they want. Employers can advertise their opportunities and find the skilled workers they need.

Campus WorkLink, a member of Industry Canada's SkillNet.ca, is a partnership between Industry Canada and The Canadian Association of Career Educators and Employers, which represents the several hundred career/placement services on campuses across Canada.

For more information, visit the Web site or contact:

Campus WorkLink
Tel: *1 800 930-9643* (toll-free)
Fax: *1 800 290-0427* (toll-free)
Web site: *www.campusworklink.com* or
www.skillnet.ca

⚡ Canada WorkinfoNET

Canada's WorkinfoNET is an Internet directory of resources to help Canadians throughout the country find information about job opportunities, career planning and occupations, planning and financing post-secondary education, entrepreneurship, and continuous learning and skills development.

For more information, visit the Web site or contact:

Canada WorkinfoNET
110-240 Catherine Street
Ottawa, ON K2P 2G8
Fax: *(613) 234-7479*
E-mail: *feedback@workinfonet.ca*
Web site: *www.workinfonet.ca*

⚡ Career Mall

Career Mall is an exclusive job placement and resumé service for the 33 000 members of the Canadian Professional Sales Association.

Web site: *www.cpsa.com/html/career_mall.asp*

⚡ Electronic Labour Exchange

The Electronic Labour Exchange (ELE) is a skills-matching system designed to help employers and workers connect on-line.

When you enter ELE as a job seeker, you first choose a job category under which you would like to be listed. Then, based on that category, you fill out a checklist of your skills and qualifications. When you're done, ELE tries to match your skills with an employer who has a position that requires those skills. If there are no job openings at the time, you can choose to advertise your skills profile to employers visiting the site.

Electronic Labour Exchange: *www.ele-spe.org*

Human Resources Development Canada Offices

If you're looking for a job or information on employment initiatives, these offices may be able to help you. The offices list job opportunities, provide employment counselling and labour market information, and offer a computerized career and education information system to help you with your career-related decisions.

The offices are open year-round. **For more information** and publications, contact your local Human Resources Development Canada office. Check the Government of Canada pages of your local telephone directory for the nearest office or call the Youth Info Line.

Youth Info Line: *1 800 935-5555* (toll-free)

Human Resources Development Canada Offices for Students

Open during the summer months, these offices help students find jobs and employers find workers. Students can drop in to check out the job opportunities or talk to the Summer Employment Officers — who are students themselves. Information is also available on various federally and provincially sponsored programs.

Through the offices' group information sessions, students learn how to look for a job, write a resumé and get ready for an interview. Information is also available on wage levels and labour laws. This program is part of the Student Summer Job Action component of Canada's Youth Employment Strategy.

In the spring, visit a Human Resources Development Canada (HRDC) Office for Students near you. Some offices are open on a year-round basis. These offices are called Hire a Student Centres in Alberta, Student/Youth Human Resource Centres in Manitoba and HRDC Student Centres in New Brunswick.

For more information, contact your local HRDC office. Check the Government of Canada section of your telephone directory for the nearest office or call the Youth Info Line.

Youth Info Line: *1 800 935-5555* (toll-free)

 **Job Bank**

Looking for work? Job Bank helps you search through lists of jobs available in communities across Canada. Updated throughout the day, Job Bank is available through all Human Resources Development Canada offices and provincial government offices as well as through several public locations such as libraries and shopping centres. It is also available on the Internet.

Job Bank: *http://jb-ge.hrdc-drhc.gc.ca*

Looking for a Job? A Guide for Youth

This booklet can help you improve your job-search skills and develop a step-by-step plan for landing a job. It shows you where to start, how to market yourself and what's out there in the world of work. It gives helpful hints on preparing for interviews, making the right impression during interviews and following up afterwards. (Cat. No. Y-140-01-00E)

For more information, or to order a copy, contact:

Youth Communications
Human Resources Development Canada
140 Promenade du Portage, 4th Floor
Hull, QC K1A 0J9
Fax: *(819) 953-5186*
Web site: *http://youth.hrdc-drhc.gc.ca/publication/looking/home.html*

Looking for Work in the Aviation Sector?

The Canadian Aviation Maintenance Council (CAMC) Job Mart is a new on-line recruitment service developed to meet the demands of the rapidly growing aviation maintenance industry.

A member of Industry Canada's SkillNet.ca network of job and career information Web sites, the CAMC Job Mart shares labour market information with employers and job seekers. Of interest to those just entering the aviation maintenance field, it also benefits experienced professionals, offering a Web-based tool that helps job seekers find work in their field, either across the city or across the country.

For more information, visit the Web site or contact:

Canadian Aviation Maintenance Council
Tel: *(613) 727-8272*
Fax: *(613) 727-7018*
E-mail: *brianblc@camc.ca*
Web site: *http://jobmart.camc.ca* or
　　　　www.skillnet.ca

Nurses@work: Career Opportunities for Nurses

Finding the right job in a health care facility can be a challenge. In partnership with Industry Canada's SkillNet.ca, the Canadian Nurses Association has introduced Nurses@work, the first central on-line recruiting registry of its kind for nurses.

Nurses@work is an effective way to search the job market. The site makes it easier for nurses to find work, whether they are searching across town or across Canada.

For more information, visit the Web site or contact:

Canadian Nurses Association
Tel: *(613) 237-2159* ext. 302
Fax: *(613) 237-3520*
E-mail: *nbartlett@cna-nurses.ca*
Web site: *www.nursesatwork.com* or
　　　　www.skillnet.ca

> Check out the *Career Information Tools* section of
> this publication to find out about other resources and
> services that may be of interest to job seekers.

Skill Building

This brochure is designed to help high-school students describe
their personal skills and aptitudes in a business language
when preparing for a job interview or writing a resumé.
(Cat. No. Y-112-01-93)

For more information, contact:

Human Resources Development Canada
Public Enquiries Centre
140 Promenade du Portage
Hull, QC K1A 0J9
Fax: *(819) 953-7260*
Web site: *www.hrdc-drhc.gc.ca/career-carriere*

SkillNet.ca

SkillNet.ca is Canada's fastest growing network of job and career
information Web sites. A one-stop shopping site for jobs and career-
related information, SkillNet.ca is an expanding partnership of inte-
grated recruitment services. These include colleges and universities
(entry-level jobs) as well as partners in the health, arts and culture,
education, aviation, and volunteer sectors. Many more partner sites
are under development.

Today, more than 170 000 job seekers use SkillNet.ca's resources to
browse over 2500 advertised employment opportunities each month.
Additional on-line services for job seekers include information on
training and educational opportunities, tips on how to write winning
resumés, and information on and access to over 40 national youth
employment programs.

More than 40 000 registered employers use SkillNet.ca as a quick
and effective way to advertise full-time, part-time, summer and
internship opportunities. Last year, employers requested more than
163 000 resumés through the SkillNet.ca family of recruitment
sites, and each month the network receives over 2.6 million page
hits.

Visit the Web site for more information, or call, fax or e-mail one of the following contacts:

Web site: *www.skillnet.ca*

Allan Schweyer
Tel: *(613) 990-3318*
Fax: *(613) 941-4940*
E-mail: *schweyer.allan@ic.gc.ca*

Janet Caroleo
Tel: *(613) 998-1301*
Fax: *(613) 941-4940*
E-mail: *caroleo.janet@ic.gc.ca*

 Talent Gallery

Looking for work in the cultural sector? An innovative on-line recruitment network is now available to help artists, creators, producers, technicians and administrators — all members of Canada's cultural labour force — find jobs and recruit employees.

Developed through a partnership between the Cultural Human Resources Council and Industry Canada's SkillNet.ca, this Web-based resource is revolutionizing the way cultural workers and their employers are brought together.

For more information, visit the Web site or contact:

Cultural Human Resources Council
17 York Street, Suite 201
Ottawa, ON K1N 9J6
Tel: *(613) 562-1535*
Fax: *(613) 562-2982*
E-mail: *info@culturalhrc.ca*
Web site: *www.culturalhrc.ca*

🔆 Volunteer Opportunities Exchange

Volunteering is a great way to develop your skills. The Volunteer Opportunities Exchange (VOE) is an innovative Internet tool that helps agencies looking for volunteers connect with people seeking volunteer opportunities. Developed in partnership with Human Resources Development Canada and Industry Canada's SkillNet.ca, the goal is to strengthen the capacity of Canada's voluntary sector.

The VOE is an exciting tool that goes beyond the traditional key-word search — it is a unique skills- and interest-based matching system on the Internet. Agencies looking for volunteers can create profiles of opportunities they wish to fill based on skills, interests and geographic location. Volunteers seeking positions can create similar profiles. The VOE will use this information to match the available opportunities with a database of available volunteers.

For more information about the VOE and volunteering, please contact:

Volunteer Canada
430 Gilmour Street
Ottawa, ON K2P 0R8
Tel: *1 800 670-0401* (toll-free)
Fax: *(613) 231-6725*
E-mail: *volunteer.canada@sympatico.ca*
Web: *www.voe-reb.org*

🔆 WorkSearch

If you're looking for work, WorkSearch is the place to start. WorkSearch is an easy-to-use Internet site designed to guide you through the process of looking for work. It will help you overcome almost any snag — you can assess your skills and interests, connect to job listings across the country or find help selling yourself with features such as an on-line resumé maker.

You can also learn about occupations and trends, what kind of training you may need, and what it takes to be self-employed.

WorkSearch: *www.worksearch.gc.ca*

⚡ Youth Resource Network of Canada

This one-stop shopping source provides information to help with the decisions you need to make regarding skills development, work experience and your career. You can reach over 3500 sites at a single Internet address and get information on:

- job preparation techniques (e.g., preparing a resumé and/or a cover letter);
- job opportunities (full-time, summer, internship and international);
- financial assistance available for students;
- Youth Info Fairs and other events; and
- programs and services (governmental, non-governmental and international exchanges).

For more information, contact:

Youth Info Line: *1 800 935-5555* (toll-free)
Web site: *www.youth.gc.ca*

Skills Development and Learning Opportunities

Aboriginal Education and Opportunities Manual

Used by students, libraries, corporations and government departments, this manual lists over 500 post-secondary institutions across Canada and provides information on scholarships and training opportunities with an Aboriginal focus. Over 200 pages, the publication lists educational institutions by province, provides a brief description of each course and directs readers to valuable contacts for more information.

To order a copy, contact:

CANDO
10404 66th Avenue, Suite 200
Edmonton, AB T6H 5R6
Tel: *1 800 463-9300* (toll-free)
Fax: *(780) 429-7487*
E-mail: *jgariepy@edo.ca*
Web site: *www.edo.ca*

Aboriginal Friendship Centre Program

The Aboriginal Friendship Centre Program is designed to improve the quality of life for Aboriginal peoples residing in or travelling through urban communities. It provides operational support to the National Association of Friendship Centres and the 99 Friendship Centres located in Canada's urban centres.

Friendship Centres provide community-based, culturally sensitive programs and services in many areas, including human resource development, health/healing, employment, justice and recreation. The program is administered by the National Association of Friendship Centres.

For more information, contact:

National Association of Friendship Centres
275 MacLaren Street
Ottawa, ON K0A 0L9
Tel: *(613) 563-4844*
Fax: *(613) 594-3428*
E-mail: *nafcgen@nafc-aboriginal.com*
Web site: *www.nafc-aboriginal.com*

Canada's SchoolNet

Canada's SchoolNet is designed to promote the effective use of information technology in learning and to foster the development of the employability skills Canadians need to compete in the knowledge-based economy. A strong alliance of public-, private- and volunteer-sector partners stand behind this collaborative initiative.

In March 1999, through SchoolNet's collaboration with ministries of education, school boards, education associations, schools, teachers, students, parents and the private sector, Canada became the first country in the world to connect all its schools and public libraries to the information highway.

SchoolNet continues to work with the provinces and the private sector to extend connectivity from schools to the classroom to bring the benefits of the information highway to Canadian learners. By the end of this phase of the SchoolNet initiative, 250 000 computers will be connected — an equivalent of one per classroom.

SchoolNet's future direction is to provide classrooms with access to multimedia service capabilities. The goal is for users to be able to access over 20 000 on-line learning projects.

For more information, please contact:

Canada's SchoolNet
Industry Canada
155 Queen Street, 4th Floor
Ottawa, ON K1A 0H5
Tel: *1 800 575-9200* (toll-free)
E-mail: *schoolnet@ic.gc.ca*
Web site: *www.schoolnet.ca*

# Canadian Cadet Organizations

If you are between the ages of 12 and 18 and are interested in a challenging experience, the Sea, Army or Air cadets is the place for you. By joining, you become one of the 54 000 cadets who participate in exciting and active training during the school year. There is also adventurous training available at summer camps (for which you would receive an allowance). These programs are free of charge.

Depending on which element you choose to join, you may participate in sailing and seamanship activities with Sea cadets, hiking expeditions and rappelling with Army cadets, or flying and gliding exercises with Air cadets. All cadets have the opportunity to participate in ceremonial parades, music and sports that help build leadership skills and self-confidence.

Successful cadets are eligible for financial scholarships, provincial and international exchanges, and other advanced training courses. Employment opportunities are also available during the summer period if you are 16 years of age and above.

Although you wear a military-style uniform, you are not a member of the Canadian Forces and are not required to join. Cadets do benefit, however, from the background and experience of the 4500 officers of the Cadet Instructors Cadre — specially trained youth leaders who stand ready to provide you with challenging experiences and activities.

For more information and the location of the Sea, Army or Air cadet corps and squadron nearest you, call:

Navy League of Canada	*1 800 375-NAVY (375-6289)*
Army Cadet League of Canada	*1 877 ARMYCAD (276-9223)*
Air Cadet League of Canada	*1 877 I CAN FLY (422-6359)*

You can also write to us or visit our Web site:

Directorate of Cadets
National Defence Headquarters
Major General George R. Pearkes Building
101 Colonel By Drive
Ottawa, ON K1A 0K2
Fax: *(613) 992-8956*
Web site: *www.cadetscanada.org*

Skills Development and Learning Opportunities

Canadian 4-H Council Programs

Council programs support the 4-H movement in Canada in the promotion of responsible citizenship, leadership, careers in agriculture,
technology transfer and other pressing issues facing today's rural
communities. The Council organizes and coordinates national and
international conferences, exchanges, and scholarships for the
benefit of 4-H members — who can be between 8 and 21 years
of age (varies depending on the province).

For more information, contact:

Canadian 4-H Council
Central Experimental Farm
930 Carling Avenue
Building #26
Ottawa, ON K1A 0C6
Tel: *(613) 234-4448*
Fax: *(613) 234-1112*
E-mail: *afriend@4-h-canada.ca*
Web site: *www.4-h-canada.ca*

Certified Economic Developer Program

The Certified Economic Developer (C.E.D.) designation is for anyone
working — or wanting to work — in the Aboriginal economic
development field. Occupations in this field include:

- Economic Development Officer;
- Community Economic Development Officer; and
- Loans Officer with an Aboriginal Capital corporation, Aboriginal
  bank or trust company, or Aboriginal Community Futures
  Organization.

The C.E.D. designation provides a national standard of competency
development and professional recognition for anyone working in
Aboriginal economic development.

For more information or an application form for the C.E.D. Program, contact:

CANDO
10404 66th Avenue, Suite 200
Edmonton, AB T6H 5R6
Tel: *1 800 463-9300* (toll-free)
Fax: *(780) 429-7487*
E-mail: *cando@ccinet.ab.ca*
Web site: *www.edo.ca*

Database on Education and Training Programs

Are you interested in educational programs and learning opportunities that prepare you for a career in the dynamic, fast-paced apparel manufacturing industry?

While most people are fashion conscious, few stop to reflect on the employment opportunities in the industry that makes the garments they like to wear. Yet, like any other product manufacturer, companies in apparel manufacturing offer careers in a full range of functions, from design and product development through production (and its supervision), sales, marketing, finance/accounting, administration and management.

The Apparel Human Resources Council has prepared a database on the programs offered across the country. Updated on a regular basis, the tables are accessible on our Web site.

For more information, contact:

Apparel Human Resources Council
130 Slater Street, Suite 1050
Ottawa, ON K1P 6E2
Tel: *(613) 567-4144*
Fax: *(613) 567-4147*
E-mail: *database@apparel-hrc.org*
Web site: *www.apparel-hrc.org*

First Nations and Inuit Science and Technology Camp Program

This program promotes science and technology as career choices. It supports science camps that provide First Nations and Inuit youth living on-reserve and in recognized Inuit communities with first-hand experience in various science and technology disciplines. Eligible youth are in grades 6 to 13 (elementary or secondary).

The program provides funds to First Nations and Inuit organizations to either run a science camp or provide sponsorship allowing First Nations and Inuit students to attend existing camps with a focus on science and technology.

For more information, please contact your band council or hamlet office, or the nearest regional office of the Department of Indian Affairs and Northern Development (DIAND). Information is also available on the Internet at the following Web sites:

Web site: *www.inac.gc.ca/youth/index.html* (DIAND)
www.ayn.ca (Aboriginal Youth Network)

First Nations SchoolNet

First Nations SchoolNet gives First Nations communities the opportunity to use exciting new technologies by providing the schools in these communities with an affordable high-speed connection to the Internet via DirecPC™ satellite terminals.

The installation and use of the equipment provided by the First Nations SchoolNet program is also supported by a network of help desks located in First Nations organizations or Aboriginal businesses across the country.

All eligible schools (i.e., schools under federal jurisdiction) receive information packages on the program. If they are interested in participating, they contact SchoolNet to make arrangements. Equipment is then sent to the schools and contact is made with the closest help desk to help support the installations. Funding mechanisms are also put in place to provide support for Internet access and long-distance expenses (where applicable).

First Nations SchoolNet also supports the development of the First Peoples' Web pages on SchoolNet, where you can find unique Aboriginal curriculum resources in English, Cree and Syllabics as well as cultural collections, profiles of Aboriginal organizations and communities, and much more.

For more information, please contact:

First Nations SchoolNet
Industry Canada
155 Queen Street, 4th Floor
Ottawa, ON K1A 0H5
Tel: *1 800 575-9200* (toll-free)
E-mail: *schoolnet@ic.gc.ca*
Web site: *www.schoolnet.ca/aboriginal*

Forum for Young Canadians

Are you between the ages of 16 and 19 with an interest in how a parliamentary system of government functions? The Forum for Young Canadians gives young people from all parts of Canada an opportunity to come to Ottawa to learn about the role of Parliament and the dynamics of the decision-making process.

As a participant, you will become better informed and will increase your understanding of other regions of the country. There are four sessions in Ottawa — each one week long — given every year.

Applications must be received at the Forum for Young Canadians office by November 15. The application form is available at secondary schools and CEGEPs across Canada, and on the Internet.

For more information, contact:

Forum for Young Canadians
124 O'Connor Street, Suite 400
Ottawa, ON K1P 5M9
Tel: *(613) 233-4086*
Fax: *(613) 233-2351*
E-mail: *forum@forum.ca*
Web site: *www.forum.ca*

Information on the Government of Canada

This service connects Canadians to government. When you need information about programs and services, new initiatives or official publications, call us toll-free or visit our Web site. It's easy. Your primary access point to the Government of Canada is only a toll-free phone call or mouse click away.

Information on the Government of Canada
Tel: 1 8ØØ O-Canada (1 800 622-6232)
Web site: *www.canada.gc.ca*

Government of Canada
Publications
Tel: *1 800 635-7943*
Web site: *http://publications.pwgsc.gc.ca*
TTY/TDD: *1 800 465-7735*

Information Technology Professional Program

Developed in partnership with Human Resources Development Canada, industry, colleges and universities, the Information Technology Professional (ITP) Program is designed to address the chronic shortage of trained information technology professionals. The program is an integration of real-life business simulation, lectures, project-based assignments and hands-on sessions.

ITP students are university or college graduates who are interested in pursuing rewarding careers within the rapidly expanding information technology sector. ITP graduates are well-educated, motivated professionals with diverse skill sets in business and organizational effectiveness, technical applications, and inter-personal communications.

Interested organizations can contribute to this program by becoming advisory committee members, offering three-month work-term opportunities, providing job opportunities, or establishing a scholarship or bursary for students.

For more information, contact:

Software Human Resource Council
Information Technology Professional Program
National Office
30 Metcalfe Street, Suite 400
Ottawa, ON K1P 5L4
Tel: *(613) 237-8551*
Fax: *(613) 230-3490*
E-mail: *info@shrc.ca*
Web site: *http://itp.shrc.ca*

Journal of Aboriginal Economic Development

This journal, the only one of its kind in Canada, features the latest information on Aboriginal economic development. Published by Captus Press and the Council for the Advancement of Native Development Officers, the journal includes examples provided by economic practitioners as well as book reviews and special features. Always insightful, the journal keeps economic developers informed about their field.

To subscribe, contact:

Captus Press
York University Campus
4700 Keele Street
North York, ON M3J 1P3
Tel: *(416) 736-5537*
Fax: *(416) 736-5793*
Web site: *www.captus.com*

Junior Canadian Rangers

If you are between the ages of 12 and 18, live in a remote and isolated community, and are interested in a challenging experience while learning about your traditional culture, the Junior Canadian Rangers (JCR) Programme is the place for you.

By joining the JCR Programme, you will enjoy a variety of activities, including hunting, fishing, living off the land, and learning about native spirituality, local dialects and traditional arts. You will also learn Ranger skills such as first aid and navigation in the North. On top of that, you may take part in citizenship activities, learn about healthy living and acquire other useful life skills. These activities will help you gain a better understanding of your culture while developing self-confidence and leadership skills.

Although you will wear a Ranger-styled uniform, you are not a Canadian Ranger or a member of the Canadian Forces. Junior Canadian Rangers benefit, however, from the background and experience of the Canadian Rangers, the elders, and the members of the local communities who will provide you with challenging experiences and activities. As such, community support is the cornerstone of the JCR Programme. The JCR Programme is free of charge.

For more information on the JCR Programme, please contact:

Junior Canadian Rangers
Directorate General Reserves and Cadets
National Defence Headquarters
101 Colonel By Drive
Ottawa, ON K1A 0K2
Tel: *(613) 995-9524*
Fax: *(613) 992-8956*

 **Katimavik**

Funded by the Department of Canadian Heritage, Katimavik is a national youth volunteer service. It allows groups of Canadians aged 17 to 21 who can speak both English and French to experience their country, serve the community, learn to work together as a group, and develop leadership and communication skills.

Katimavik participants spend 36 weeks living in groups of 11 and working on community projects in three different locations — two predominantly anglophone and one predominantly francophone. They take part in a wide variety of skills-development activities such as environmental projects, volunteer work, community living, learning about computers and second-language learning.

For further information, contact:

Katimavik
Tel: *1 888 525-1503* (toll-free)
E-mail: *katimavik@camitel.com*
Web site: *www.katimavik.org*

> If you're interested in volunteering as a way to build on your current skills while gaining work experience and self-confidence, check out the Volunteer Opportunities Exchange listing in the *Job-Search Tools* section of this publication.

Office of Learning Technologies

As a partner in building a culture of lifelong learning, the Government of Canada established the Office of Learning Technologies (OLT) within Human Resources Development Canada. The OLT's role is to raise awareness about the opportunities, challenges and benefits of technology-based learning and to act as a catalyst for innovation in this arena.

Major initiatives at the OLT include the Learning Technologies Initiative, the Community Learning Networks Initiative, and Learning Technologies and the Workplace — an extensive Web site on learning technologies, research and publications.

To learn more about the OLT, log on to the Web site or contact:

Office of Learning Technologies
Human Resources Development Canada
15 Eddy Street, Ground Floor
Hull, QC K1A 0M5
Tel: *(819) 953-0300*
Fax: *(819) 997-6777*
Web site: *http://olt-bta.hrdc-drhc.gc.ca*

 # Open House Canada

Through its Open House Canada component, the Department of Canadian Heritage provides funding to a number of national non-profit organizations that administer reciprocal group exchanges or national forums for young Canadians between the ages of 14 and 19.

These learning opportunities are intended to increase young people's knowledge, appreciation and respect for the diversity of Canadian society and its institutions. They are also aimed at encouraging active citizen participation in activities that contribute to national harmony. The funding provided by the Department helps cover part of the transportation costs of eligible participants.

For more information, contact:

Youth Participation Program
Department of Canadian Heritage
Ottawa, ON K1A 0M5
Tel: *(819) 994-1544*
Fax: *(819) 997-8777*
Web site: *www.pch.gc.ca/yp-pj/index.html*

Peer Helper Programs for Out-of-the-Mainstream Youth

This information sheet will be useful to anyone working with at-risk youth and wanting to create, improve or maintain peer helper programs. It provides a summary of the factors to consider when implementing a peer helper program. It also describes three basic kinds of programs, lists factors that help make any program effective and gives a number of references.

For more information, contact:

Health Canada
Childhood and Youth Division
Health Promotions and Programs Branch
Address Locator: 1909C2
Ottawa, ON K1A 1B4
Tel: *(613) 957-7804*
Fax: *(613) 954-5568*
E-mail: *familychild@www.hc-sc.gc.ca*
Web site: *www.hc-sc.gc.ca/childhood-youth*

 SchoolNet GrassRoots Program

By supporting the development of innovative on-line learning projects, the GrassRoots Program enables Canadian teachers and students to build the knowledge tools they need, contribute to their communities, raise awareness of global issues, establish partnerships and communication links around the world, and take charge of their future while taking advantage of the vast potential of the information highway.

GrassRoots offers funding to schools to create and implement innovative and interactive learning projects on the Internet that:

- foster the acquisition of academic, employability and computer skills in Canadian youth;
- build unique and relevant Canadian content on the Internet;
- integrate information and communication technologies into learning; and
- facilitate increased connectivity, usage and training opportunities.

Teacher-designed and tailored to the learning needs of students in today's classrooms, GrassRoots projects are a unique and valuable resource. Through its Web site, the GrassRoots Program provides a vehicle to showcase the best practices of Canadian teachers and students integrating information and communication technologies at the classroom level.

For more information, please contact:

SchoolNet GrassRoots Program
Industry Canada
155 Queen Street, 4th Floor
Ottawa, ON K1A 0H5
Tel: *1 800 575-9200* (toll-free)
E-mail: *schoolnet@ic.gc.ca*
Web site: *www.schoolnet.ca/grassroots*

Urban Multipurpose Aboriginal Youth Centres

This initiative provides urban Aboriginal youth with accessible, Aboriginal community-based, culturally relevant and supportive projects, programs, services, and professional and peer counselling. The goal is to enhance the economic, social and personal prospects of Aboriginal youth. This initiative serves the needs of Aboriginal youth between 15 and 24 years of age who live off-reserve in urban or northern communities with a population of 1000 or over — regardless of status, culture or gender.

For more information, contact:

National Association of Friendship Centres
275 MacLaren Street
Ottawa, ON K2P 0L9
Tel: *(613) 563-4844*
Fax: *(613) 594-3428*

Métis National Council
350 Sparks Street, Suite 201
Delta Hotel Office Tower
Ottawa, ON K1R 7S8
Tel: *(613) 232-3216*
Fax: *(613) 232-4262*

Inuit Tapirisat of Canada
170 Laurier Avenue, Suite 510
Ottawa, ON K1P 5V5
Tel: *(613) 238-8181*
Fax: *(613) 994-5252*

When it comes to developing skills, there's nothing like on-the-job training! Take a look at the *Travel, Work Experience Opportunities* and *Work Experience Opportunities — International* sections of this publication for other work- and career-related learning opportunities.

Travel

Agence Québec/Wallonie–Bruxelles pour la jeunesse

If you are between 18 and 30, a Canadian citizen or permanent resident, and have lived in Quebec for at least the past year, you may be eligible to attend a training program in Belgium.

An agency for international co-operation between Belgium and Quebec, Agence Québec/Wallonie-Bruxelles pour la jeunesse (AQWBJ) offers an opportunity to develop knowledge and apply it in an international setting. Training is available in economic and cultural development, environment, communications, and science and technology. Agency specialists will help you choose the right kind of course and prepare the proposal. Regardless of the field of study or activity, AQWBJ will provide supervision throughout the training.

Training areas include information, exploration and/or research, co-operation, on-the-job training, professional and social immersion, and invitations to special events, conferences, conventions and festivals. Most of the courses last two weeks.

The program requires an expenditure of between $250 and $425 by the trainee. In turn, the agency provides Montréal-Brussels return airfare, medical hospital insurance and a per diem allowance of $40 for up to 14 days. This represents three quarters of the cost of the trip.

For more information, contact:

Agence Québec/Wallonie-Bruxelles pour la jeunesse
1441 Réne-Lévesque Blvd. West, Room 301
Montréal, QC H3G 1T7
Tel: *(514) 873-4355*
Fax: *(514) 873-1538*

Be Prepared. . . Take Charge

- Make sure you are carrying a valid passport.
- Check that the expiry date of your passport is well beyond your return date.
- Make two copies of the identification page of your passport. Leave one copy with a friend or relative at home. Bring the second copy with you on your trip.
- Protect your passport at all times.
- Carry your passport on you in a money belt or lock it in your hotel safe.
- In some countries you may have to surrender your passport to a foreign government official or a hotel employee. If you don't get it back in a reasonable time, inform the nearest Canadian embassy or consulate.
- Carry the photocopy of the identification page separately from the original when you travel. This can help with the replacement process if your passport is lost or stolen.

 ## Canada–Austria Intra- and Partner- Company Training Program

This program seeks to support Canadian and Austrian firms in developing business links between the two countries by facilitating intra- and partner-company training. Canadian workers can travel to Austria to receive or provide training, which could include skills upgrading, familiarization with current business practices and, in some cases, formal classroom training.

The Embassy of Austria or an Austrian consulate in Canada can issue a residence permit. This may be a transfer licence that is valid for four months or a clearance certificate that is valid for up to 36 weeks.

To participate in this program, you must possess a Canadian passport that is valid for a period of three months beyond the termination of activities under the program. You must also be 18 to 30 years old at the time of application — except in those cases where the authorities of both countries decide to raise the maximum age to 35 years or higher. You are also required to have a round-trip airplane ticket and enough funds to meet your needs during your stay in Austria. If accepted, you should also be prepared to undergo a medical examination before starting your training — if this is required by law for the activity in question — as well as to pay a visa or program participation fee.

For more information, contact:

Embassy of the Republic of Austria
445 Wilbrod Street
Ottawa, ON K1N 6M7
Tel: *(613)789-1444*
Fax: *(613) 789-3431*

 # Canada–Netherlands Student Working Holiday Program

Experience life in the Netherlands while engaging in temporary (four months), career-related employment. Areas of interest vary and include industry, commerce, science and technology, tourism, agriculture, and horticulture.

The Working Holiday Program is open to Canadian citizens or permanent residents 18 to 30 years of age. To participate, you must be registered at a post-secondary institution and have either a written job offer from an employer in the Netherlands or friends/relatives who can help you find a job or provide accommodation. As well, you must prove that you have sufficient funds for the trip.

Applications are accepted throughout the year but should be made at least a few months before the desired departure date.

To obtain an information brochure and more information, contact:

Stichting Uitwisseling
Attention: Rosemieke van de Meerendonk
24 Goulding Crescent
Kanata, ON K2K 2N9
Tel: *(613) 599-6316*
Fax: *(613) 599-9397*
Web site: *www.uitwisseling.nl*

Canada–Taiwan Student Exchange Program

Sponsored by Human Resources Development Canada, this program provides support for undergraduate university students to undertake a short-term study placement in Taiwan.

For more information, visit the Association of Universities and Colleges of Canada Web site or contact:

Association of Universities and Colleges of Canada
350 Albert Street, Suite 600
Ottawa, ON K1R 1B1
Tel: *(613) 563-1236*
Fax: *(613) 563-9745*
E-mail: *jgallagh@aucc.ca*
Web site: *www.aucc.ca*

Canadian Association of University Teachers of German Workstudent Program (Germany)

If you are 18 to 30 years old, able to work in German and enrolled in a Canadian university or college that is a member of the Canadian Association of University Teachers of German (CAUTG), you may be eligible for the Workstudent Program.

The program provides two months of work experience, June 1 to July 31, primarily in the hotel/restaurant industry, and the opportunity to improve German-language skills and experience German culture. About four weeks are left for independent travel. A travel subsidy may be available.

Applications are due by November 30 of each year. Apply through the German department of a Canadian university or college. Manpower Germany will make the final decision. Information sheets and posters are available through German studies programs at CAUTG-member universities and colleges.

For more information, contact:

Canadian Association of University Teachers of German
Department of Germanic and Slavic Studies
Brock University
St. Catharines, ON L2S 3A1
Tel: *(905) 688-5550* ext. 3312

International 4-H Trade Awareness Program

Are you a 4-H member? Do you want to expand your agricultural knowledge to an international level? How about attending a world-class food fair?

Sponsored by Agriculture and Agri-Food Canada, the International 4-H Trade Awareness Program is designed to enhance the awareness of agri-food trade issues among 4-H youth interested in the agriculture sector and to encourage an interest in working in this area in the future. Ten provincial winners are chosen every year and one grand prizewinner is sent to one of the biggest and most popular international food fairs held each fall.

For more information, contact your local 4-H office or:

Canadian 4-H Council
Central Experimental Farm
930 Carling Avenue
Building #26
Ottawa, ON K1A 0C6
Tel: *(613) 234-4448*
Fax: *(613) 234-1112*
Web site: *www.4-h-canada.ca*

Obtaining a Passport

Application forms may be obtained from any passport office or post office. Full details on the requirements are provided with each application form.

You must complete both sides of the application form, provide two current photographs, and have the application form and one photograph signed by an eligible guarantor. You must also provide original evidence of Canadian citizenship, any previous Canadian passport, certificate of identity or refugee travel document issued to you in the last five years, and the fee of $60. You may pay the fee in cash (do not mail cash), by money order (postal or bank), by certified cheque or bank draft (payable to the Receiver General for Canada), or by VISA, MasterCard or debit card.

If you reside in an area with a passport office, you are encouraged to submit your application in person. (Applications submitted in person usually take five working days to process. Applications submitted by mail usually take 10 working days.) Check the Government of Canada pages of your telephone directory for the address of your nearest passport office. If there is no passport office in your area, mail your application in a standard business envelope to:

The Passport Office
Department of Foreign Affairs and International Trade
Ottawa, ON K1A 0G3

For more information, or for assistance in completing your form, you may contact:

Ottawa-Hull and area:	*(819) 994-3500*
Montréal and area:	*(514) 283-2152*
Toronto and area:	*(416) 973-3251*
Greater Vancouver area:	*(604) 586-2500*
Toll-free:	*1 800 567-6868*
Web site: *www.ppt.gc.ca*	

Protecting Your Passport

Your passport is a valuable document. Do not leave it unattended in your baggage, automobile, hotel room or elsewhere. Keep it in a safe place on your person, in an inside pocket or in your purse.

When you receive your passport, sign your name on page 3 in the space provided and fill in the section on page 4 for your address and a person to contact in case of emergency. It is recommended that you provide the name of someone who would not normally accompany you on a trip. If your address changes, make sure you neatly amend the information on page 4.

If your passport is lost or stolen, report the loss or theft as soon as possible to the local police and passport office or to the nearest Canadian mission. A replacement passport (which may be valid for a limited period only) may be authorized. However, there are strict requirements to be met, including the submission of a completed application form, photographs, fee, documentary proof of Canadian citizenship and a declaration regarding the loss or theft.

Working Holiday Program (Australia)

Travel in Australia with short-term work to support your stay. The Working Holiday Program is designed for Canadians between the ages of 18 and 25 with a valid passport, a return travel ticket and sufficient funds to travel in Australia on their own. It allows Canadians to spend a maximum of 12 months working, on an incidental basis, to support their stay in Australia. Work can generally be found in the service industries and in farming. Employment with one employer for more than three months is not permitted.

Apply at least eight weeks before the proposed departure date. Application for the visa must be made to a diplomatic or consular mission of the Government of Australia in Canada.

For more information, contact:

Australian High Commission
50 O'Connor Street, Suite 710
Ottawa, ON K1P 6L2
Tel: *(613) 236-0841*
Fax: *(613) 236-4376*
Web site: *www.immi.gov.au/allforms/temp-whm.htm*

 # Working Holiday Program (Canada–Japan)

Are you interested in travelling and working in Japan? If you are a Canadian citizen currently residing in Canada and are between the ages of 18 and 30, you may be eligible for the Working Holiday Program in Japan.

This program promotes cultural understanding and co-operation, and gives young Canadians the opportunity to visit Japan for an extended holiday and to supplement their travel expenses through occasional employment. Many find employment teaching English, either at language schools or by tutoring employees in a company. There is also a demand for French-language tutoring.

You must have a return travel ticket — or sufficient funds to purchase a return ticket — and reasonable funds, including the cost of possible medical expenses, to cover your initial stay in Japan.

Apply at least eight weeks before the proposed departure date. Visa applications must be made to a diplomatic or consular mission of the Government of Japan in Canada.

For more information, contact:

Embassy of Japan
255 Sussex Drive
Ottawa, ON K1N 9E6
Tel: *(613) 241-8541*
Fax: *(613) 241-7415*
Web site: *www.embassyjapancanada.org*

Working Holiday Program (Germany)

This program provides university and college students with the opportunity to expand and enhance their overseas travel experience by working in Germany. Work does not have to be study-related.

Participants enjoy the same treatment as German nationals in all matters concerning the application of laws, regulations, and practices regarding health and working conditions. The normal working holiday exchange lasts up to three months.

To be eligible, you must be 18 to 30 years of age, a Canadian citizen, registered at a post-secondary institution and able to demonstrate a working knowledge of German. You must also have a written offer of employment from an employer in Germany before leaving Canada. The offer must state the name and location of the company, type and duration of occupation, wages, hours of work, benefits, and other terms of employment. The German Embassy and consulates in Canada can help you with your search.

Students must pay their own travel and accommodation costs. In some cases, board and lodging are provided by the employer. Visa applications must be made to a diplomatic or consular mission of the Government of the Federal Republic of Germany in Canada. Candidates can also apply through the Student Work Abroad Program (SWAP).

For more information, contact any of the following:

Embassy of the Federal Republic of Germany
Ms Regina Mittner
1 Waverley Street
Ottawa, ON K2P 0T8
Tel: *(613) 232-1101*
Fax: *(613) 594-9330*
Web site: *www.GermanEmbassyOttawa.org*

Consulate General of the Federal Republic of Germany
77 Admiral Road
Toronto, ON M5R 2L4
Tel: *(416) 925-2813/2814/2815*
Fax: *(416) 925-2818*

Consulate General of the Federal Republic of Germany
1250 René-Lévesque Blvd. West
41st Floor, Marathon Building
Montréal, QC H3B 4W8
Tel: *(514) 931-2277*
Fax: *(514) 931-7239*

Consulate General of the Federal Republic of Germany
World Trade Centre
999 Canada Place, Suite 704
Vancouver, BC V6C 3E1
Tel: *(604) 684-8377*
Fax: *(604) 684-8334*

🏃 Working Holiday Program (Ireland)

This program is designed for Canadian citizens between the ages of 18 and 30 who possess a valid passport and have sufficient funds to travel in Ireland. Participants must also have a written offer of employment from an Irish employer. The program enables Canadian young people to work in Ireland for up to four months.

You should apply for the work permit at least three months before the proposed departure date. The permit application form is available from the Department of Enterprise and Employment in Ireland.

For more information, contact:

Embassy of Ireland
130 Albert Street, Suite 1105
Ottawa, ON K1P 5G4
Tel: *(613) 233-6281*
Fax: *(613) 233-5835*

🏃 Working Holiday Program (Korea)

This program gives young Canadians an opportunity to visit Korea for an extended holiday and to meet their travel expenses through occasional employment.

To be eligible, you must be 18 to 25 years of age and a Canadian citizen currently residing in Canada. You must also possess a valid passport and a return travel ticket — or sufficient funds to purchase a return ticket — as well as sufficient funds to cover your expenses (including medical expenses) during your stay in Korea.

The initial working visa is for six months. It may be extended for a second consecutive six-month period.

For more information, please contact:

Embassy of the Republic of Korea
150 Boteler Street
Ottawa, ON K1N 5A6
Tel: *(613) 244-5010*
Fax: *(613) 244-5034*

General Consulate of the Republic of Korea
1000 Sherbrooke Street West
Suite 1710
Montréal, QC H3A 3G4
Tel: *(514) 845-3243*
Fax: *(514) 845-8517*

Consulate General of the Republic of Korea
555 Avenue Road
Toronto, ON M4V 2J7
Tel: *(416) 920-3809*
Fax: *(416) 924-7305*

Consulate General of the Republic of Korea
1066 Hastings Street West, Suite 830
Vancouver, BC V6E 3X1
Tel: *(604) 681-9581*
Fax: *(604) 681-4864*

Working Holiday Program (New Zealand)

Holiday in New Zealand with temporary employment as an incidental aspect of the holiday.

Canadian citizens between the ages of 18 and 30 are eligible for the program if they are able to satisfy the visa officer that the primary intention is to holiday in New Zealand — with employment being an incidental rather than a primary reason for the visit.

Participants must also possess a return travel ticket and sufficient funds for the first six months of their visit to New Zealand.

The goal is to increase the movement of young people between Canada and New Zealand and to strengthen the links between the two countries.

For more information, contact:

New Zealand High Commission
Metropolitan House
99 Bank Street, Suite 727
Ottawa, ON K1P 6G3
Tel: *(613) 238-5991*
Fax: *(613) 238-5707*
Web site: *www.nzhcottawa.org/*

New Zealand Consular Office
888 Dunsmuir Street, Suite 1200
Vancouver, BC V6C 3K4
Tel: *(604) 684-7388*
Fax: *(604) 684-7333*

Working Holiday Program (Sweden)

This program gives students and non-students the opportunity to expand and enhance their overseas travel experience by living and working in Sweden. The program allows you to work in Sweden for up to 12 months.

To be eligible, candidates must be 18 to 30 years of age and possess a valid Canadian passport. Employment is not limited to only one employer, place or particular field.

Applications must be submitted in person at least six to eight weeks before the intended date of arrival in Sweden. Trainees are responsible for making their own travel arrangements and for ensuring appropriate insurance coverage.

For more information, contact any of the following:

Embassy of Sweden
Mercury Court
377 Dalhousie Street
Ottawa, ON K1N 9N8
Tel: *(613) 241-8553*
Fax: *(613) 241-2277*

Consulate General of Sweden
2 Bloor Street West, Suite 1504
Toronto, ON M4W 3E2
Tel: *(416) 963-8768*
Fax: *(416) 923-8809*

Consulate General of Sweden
1188 West Georgia Street, Suite 1100
Vancouver, BC V6E 4A2
Tel: *(604) 683-5838*
Fax: *(604) 687-8237*

You'll find information about other opportunities to combine travel with work experience and/or learning in the *Work Experience Opportunities – International* and the *Skills Development and Learning Opportunities* sections of this publication.

Working Holiday Program (United Kingdom)

This program enables Canadian students and non-students to holiday in the United Kingdom for an extended period of time and to work occasionally to cover incidental expenses. No employer-specific work permit is issued to Canadians under this program. Canadian citizens can remain up to two years. Jobs are usually available in retail, offices, and pubs and other hospitality/service establishments.

To be eligible, candidates must be Commonwealth citizens 17 to 27 years of age and must demonstrate a good working knowledge of English. They must also have a valid passport and sufficient funds to travel in the United Kingdom.

Candidates should apply at least eight weeks before their proposed departure date. Application for a visa must be made to a diplomatic or consular mission of the United Kingdom in Canada. Candidates can also apply through the Student Work Abroad Program (SWAP).

For more information, contact any of the following:

British High Commission
Immigration Section
80 Elgin Street
Ottawa, ON K1P 5K7
Tel: *(613) 237-2008*
Fax: *(613) 232-2533*

British Consulate General
1000 de la Gauchetière West, Suite 4200
Montréal, QC H3B 4W5
Tel: *(514) 866-5863*
Fax: *(514) 866-0202*

British Consulate General
777 Bay Street, Suite 1910
College Park
Toronto, ON M5G 2G2
Tel: *(416) 593-1290*
Fax: *(416) 593-1229*

British Consulate General
1111 Melville Street, Suite 800
Vancouver, BC V6E 3V6
Tel: *(604) 683-4421*
Fax: *(604) 681-0693*

Work Experience Opportunities

🔆 Aboriginal Student Internship Program

The Aboriginal Student Internship Program (ASIP) offers jobs in the offices of Human Resources Development Canada. To be eligible, you must be a full-time student of North American Aboriginal ancestry returning to full-time studies in the following academic term.

To apply, you must be registered in the Federal Student Work Experience Program (FSWEP) inventory. You are strongly encouraged to apply to FSWEP by the end of December, because recruitment for ASIP positions may begin very early in the year. **You can apply** on-line at the Public Service Commission of Canada Web site. [See the FSWEP listing in this section.]

Web site: *http://jobs.gc.ca*

🔆 Accelerated Economist Training Program

The Public Service Commission (PSC) of Canada recruits and develops high-calibre university students for the Accelerated Economist Training Program (AETP).

Program participants undergo four six-month assignments at host departments with economic public-policy responsibilities. Participants are expected to gain an understanding of the Cabinet system and the decision-making process in the Canadian government. After two years, participants are eligible for mid-level positions in departments or agencies within the federal public service.

If you have completed, or are near completion of, a master's degree in economics, public administration or a related discipline with an undergraduate degree and graduate-level courses in these two specific areas, you are eligible to apply.

For general information on AETP, visit the program's Web site.

Recruitment takes place in late summer/early fall of each year. At that time of year, there are three different methods for you to find out how to apply. You may:

* consult the PSC recruitment Web site,
* visit the campus career centre at your post-secondary institution, or

- visit the nearest PSC office.

A list of our regional offices appears in the Important Addresses and Phone Numbers index.

Web site: *www.psc-cfp.gc.ca/aetp/aetp.htm* (AETP)
        http://jobs.gc.ca (PSC recruitment)

Agri-Food Science Horizons Program

Are you a recent graduate in a science-related or veterinary program? Do you want to gain meaningful research experience in the agri-food sector?

Science Horizons is designed to help up to 200 young scientists and veterinarians gain appropriate technical expertise, practical experience and expert mentoring from leading agri-food sector researchers. The goal is meaningful employment in highly skilled areas of science and technology. The focus on youth also addresses a growing concern over the aging of the research community by helping to train a new generation of scientists with the necessary multidisciplinary and project management skills to replace retiring senior scientists over the coming years.

The program is a collaborative effort in partnership with the private sector, and it is administered through Agriculture and Agri-Food Canada's 18 national research centres across Canada. Industry stakeholders are responsible for submitting research proposals for the program and providing their share of the cost of the project.

Science Horizons provides a maximum of $12 000 per participant per year — to be matched by an equal amount from the private sector. The program is part of the Government of Canada's Youth Employment Strategy.

For more information, contact:

Financial Advisor
Agriculture and Agri-Food Canada
Research Branch
Tel: *(613) 759-7793*
Fax: *(613) 759-7766*
E-mail: *bigrasa@em.agr.ca*
Web site: *www.agr.ca*

Program administrators suggest that if you are interested in participating in the Science Horizons Program, you should put your resumé on Campus WorkLink (formerly known as the National Graduate Register). This bilingual, searchable Internet database matches recruiting businesses with job-seeking students. For more information, turn to the Campus WorkLink listing in the *Job-Search Tools* section of this publication.

Canada's Digital Collections Program

Canada's Digital Collections (CDC) displays a wealth of on-line resources on Canada's history, geography, culture, and science and technology achievements. One of the largest sources of Canadian content on the Internet, CDC houses over 300 Web sites created by more than 2000 young Canadians working under contract to Industry Canada. The program is funded by the Government of Canada's Youth Employment Strategy.

CDC's fascinating Web sites range from the treasures of federal institutions such as the National Library, the National Archives and the Museum of Civilization, to the local histories and way of life of Canadian communities.

For further information, or to request bookmarks or posters, contact:

Canada's Digital Collections Program
Tel: *1 800 465-7766* (toll-free)
E-mail: *parent.guy@ic.gc.ca*
Web site: *http://collections.ic.gc.ca*

Career Edge

Career Edge is designed to help Canadian youth make the transition from full-time education to full-time employment. Career Edge arranges 6-, 9- or 12-month internships for university, college or high-school graduates wishing to gain experience with an established company.

A typical Career Edge intern is a graduate with strong academic credentials who lacks the relevant work experience to get a start in a chosen career. In some cases, host organizations use Career Edge as an opportunity to host interns from disciplines such as liberal or fine arts who might not have been considered in the regular recruitment process.

Career Edge is a private-sector, not-for-profit corporation established to increase the employability of Canadian youth.

For more information and an application form, browse the Career Edge Web site or contact:

Career Edge
155 University Avenue
Suite 1650
Toronto, ON M5H 3B7
Tel: *(416) 363-0003*
Toll-free: *1 888 507-3343*
Fax: *(416) 363-0888*
Web site: *www.careeredge.org*

Career Steps

Career Steps matches women who are post-secondary, science or technology graduates with potential employers. This Youth Internship Project is funded by Human Resources Development Canada through the WITT (Women in Trades and Technology) National Network, an education and advocacy organization for women in trades, technology, operations and blue-collar work.

For more information, contact:

WITT Works!/Career Steps
830 Bathurst Street
Toronto, ON M5R 3G1
Tel: *(416) 588-4368*
Toll-free: *1 877 306-9637*
Fax: *(416) 588-3063*
E-mail: *works@wittnn.com*
Web site: *www.wittnn.com/works*

Centre Internships at IDRC

These internships provide hands-on experience to promising
individuals who, through demonstrated achievements in work or
research, have shown an interest in the creation and utilization of
knowledge from an international perspective.

Interns acquire knowledge and skills by working on International
Development Research Centre (IDRC) program initiatives while
contributing their own knowledge and experience. Internship
projects must be linked to one of the program initiatives of the
IDRC program framework.

To be eligible, you must be either a Canadian citizen/permanent
resident or a national from a developing country. You must also
have some training at the graduate level.

Due to the volume of requests, applications cannot be acknowledged
individually. Candidates will be contacted if suitable internship
opportunities are available.

**Visit the Web site for more information on the program and on
deadlines for submitting applications, or contact:**

International Development Research Centre
Centre Training and Awards Unit
PO Box 8500
Ottawa, ON K1G 3H9
Tel: *(613) 236-6163* ext. 2098
Fax: *(613) 563-0815*
E-mail: *cta@idrc.ca*
Web site: *www.idrc.ca/awards*

Community Access Program

Industry Canada's Community Access Program (CAP) aims to ensure that Canadians have affordable access to the Internet and related information technologies. CAP is also integral to the Government of Canada's Youth Employment Strategy, as the program offers three-month internships and other job opportunities for over 1000 young Canadians each year.

Through CAP, youth aged 15 to 30 are hired to help connect communities across Canada to the information highway and to promote its use for local economic and social purposes. Working in Community Access Sites, particularly in rural and remote communities, CAP youth interns help small businesses, community organizations and individuals of all ages increase their knowledge of the Internet and related information technologies as well as acquire the skills to use them effectively. This work experience enables youth to gain practical knowledge and marketable skills in the rapid-growth area of information technologies. Interns also develop teaching, marketing and business skills, and build their core employability skills.

For more information, please contact:

Community Access Program
Industry Canada
155 Queen Street, 7th Floor
Ottawa, ON K1A 0H5
Tel: *1 800 268-6608* (toll-free)
E-mail: *comaccess@ic.gc.ca*
Web site: *http://cap.ic.gc.ca/*

Computers for Schools

The Computers for Schools Program repairs and refurbishes surplus computer equipment donated to the program by federal and provincial governments and private-sector organizations. The computers are then donated to schools and public libraries across Canada, with a goal of donating 250 000 during the current phase of this project.

Interested applicants will perform repair and refurbishment functions in one of the program's 68 repair centres across the country. They may also provide on-site installation/network assistance to information technology staff in local school boards.

For more information, please contact:

Computers for Schools
Industry Canada
155 Queen Street, 8th Floor
Ottawa, ON K1A 0H5
Tel: *1 800 268-6608* (toll-free)
Web site: *www.schoolnet.ca/cfs-ope*

Co-operative Education/Internships

This initiative provides students with an opportunity to gain valuable experience related to their current academic field of study. It also helps prepare them for the successful transition from school to the world of work. Post-secondary co-op internship students requiring a mandatory work term as a condition of graduation should consult their co-op coordinator on campus to find out about work-term opportunities within the Canadian public service.

Post-secondary students enrolled in a Public Service Commission-approved co-operative education or internship program are eligible to apply.

Students should contact their co-op coordinator on campus to **obtain additional information**.

Cultural Youth Internship Program

The Youth Internship Program (YIP) provides financial support to cultural organizations and businesses to help them hire young interns for 6 to 12 months. YIP is offered by the Cultural Human Resources Council, a national not-for-profit organization. This partnership program is funded by Human Resources Development Canada and the Department of Canadian Heritage under the Government of Canada's Youth Employment Strategy.

For more information, contact:

Cultural Human Resources Council
17 York Street, Suite 201
Ottawa, ON K1N 9J6
Tel: *(613) 562-1535* ext. 27
Fax: *(613) 562-2982*
E-mail: *info@culturalhrc.ca*
Web site: *www.culturalhrc.ca*

Department of National Defence Security and Defence Forum Internship Program

The Internship Program helps recent master's graduates with a background in security and defence studies obtain work experience through a year-long placement in a research or related position in a Canadian organization, excluding universities and government.

Internships are valued at up to $24 000 for 12 months (pro-rated for shorter periods). Participating organizations are encouraged to supplement this amount with additional funds. Approximately six internships are awarded each year. The internships are not renewable.

All applicants must be Canadian citizens or permanent residents at the time of application, and must hold a master's degree.

Applications must be submitted to the Association of Universities and Colleges of Canada (AUCC), which administers the internships, by February 1.

For more information and an application form, visit the AUCC Web site or contact:

Association of Universities and Colleges of Canada
Canadian Awards Program
350 Albert Street, Suite 600
Ottawa, ON K1R 1B1
Tel: *(613) 563-1236*
Fax: *(613) 563-9745*
E-mail: *awards@aucc.ca*
Web site: *www.aucc.ca*

Earth Sciences Sector Volunteer Program

Participants gain hands-on experience through assignments with earth scientists, technologists and other professionals. Assisting in the lab, the field or the library are a few of the ways participants become involved.

If you are at least 18 years of age and have an interest in science, contact the Earth Sciences Sector (ESS) of Natural Resources Canada **for more information**.

Natural Resources Canada
Earth Sciences Sector
ESS Volunteer Program Co-ordinator
601 Booth Street
Ottawa, ON K1A 0E8
Tel: *(613) 992-7362*
Fax: *(613) 947-0146*
E-mail: *dperreau@nrcan.gc.ca*

Environment Canada's Science Horizons Youth Internship

Created under the Science and Technology stream of the Government of Canada's Youth Employment Strategy, this program is a collaborative effort with Canadian universities, provinces, industry and non-governmental organizations. It encourages promising young scientists and post-secondary graduates through mentoring and coaching by experienced scientists and program managers.

Participants must be under 30 years of age and legally entitled to work in Canada. Over 100 young Canadians participate each year.

Apply by contacting the Environment Canada regional office nearest you (see the Important Addresses and Phone Numbers index for locations).

Experience Canada

Experience Canada is a national career development program designed to reduce youth unemployment and strengthen national unity by helping young graduates gain the work experience they need to qualify for the modern workplace. Eligible participants benefit from an all-expenses-paid 26-week work experience in a province or territory other than their own.

You are eligible to participate if you are:

- 18 to 29 years of age;
- out of school for at least three months;
- fluent in one of Canada's official languages;
- a graduate of high school, college, CEGEP, university or a recognized certificate course;
- unemployed or underemployed; and
- a Canadian citizen or a legal resident.

Experience Canada is a project of the Council for Canadian Unity. Primary funding comes from the private sector, with additional financial support from Human Resources Development Canada.

For more information, contact:

Experience Canada
646 Principale Avenue
Gatineau, QC J8T 5L4
Tel: *1 888 234-6618* (toll-free)
Web site: *www.experiencecanada.org*

 # Federal Public Sector Youth Internship Program

Gain experience and employability skills through a 12-month internship at a Government of Canada work site. Of the 4500 internships that have been made available over a three-year period, 50% are for high-school dropouts, 30% are for high-school graduates, and 20% are for college and university graduates.

Opportunities for graduates are listed on the Career Edge Web site, or you can call either of the two Career Edge phone numbers listed below **for more information**. Youth without a high-school diploma should contact their nearest YMCA or call the YMCA Employment Services toll-free number.

Tel: *(416) 363-0003* (Career Edge)
Toll-free: *1 888 507-3343* (Career Edge)
Toll-free: *1 800 495-8775* (YMCA Employment Services)
Web site: *www.careeredge.org*

Federal Student Work Experience Program

The Federal Student Work Experience Program offers you the opportunity to grow personally, develop new skills and learn more about how the federal government works. Students can be hired year-round — full-time or part-time during a non-academic term or part-time during the academic term.

You are eligible to apply if you are a full-time student at a university, college, CEGEP, technical institute or high school and are planning to continue full-time studies in the upcoming academic term.

There is no deadline for applying to the general inventory. However, certain departments and agencies may have established application deadlines or specific dates by which they will access the inventory.

For additional information, or to apply, consult the Public Service Commission of Canada recruitment Web site. Application forms and student guides are available from campus career centres at your university, college or CEGEP, and from Human Resources Development Canada offices and Public Service Commission of Canada offices across the country. [See the Important Addresses and Phone Numbers index in this publication for the regional office nearest you.]

Web site: *http://jobs.gc.ca*

 # First Nations and Inuit Summer Student Career Placement Program

This program is part of the Government of Canada's Student Summer Job Action initiative. It provides First Nations and Inuit students with opportunities for career-related work experience and training during the summer months. The overall purpose is to assist students in preparing for their future entry into the labour market.

Wage contributions are provided to create incremental jobs for Inuit and First Nations students on-reserve. Employers may be Inuit or First Nations governments, organizations, or businesses employing Inuit and First Nations individuals.

Students who were registered full-time during the preceding academic year and who intend to return to school on a full-time basis in the next academic year are eligible.

Eligible proposals must provide for a minimum of 30 hours of work per week and a duration of 4 to 18 weeks.

For more information, please contact the nearest regional office of the Department of Indian Affairs and Northern Development (DIAND), or visit the DIAND Web site or the Aboriginal Youth Network Web site.

Web site: *www.inac.gc.ca/youth/index.html* (DIAND)
          www.ayn.ca (Aboriginal Youth Network)

First Nations and Inuit Youth Work Experience Program

This program provides supervised work experience for out-of-school, unemployed First Nations and Inuit youths (16 to 24 years of age). The program pays minimum wage plus benefits for a period of six to nine months.

All proposals must include provision for a community-based project leader who will ensure that the youths receive the necessary mentoring, support for developing life and work skills, counselling, career development, and evaluation. Each participant works with the project leader to develop an individual learning plan that incorporates the work experience program into a longer-term plan for education and/or employment.

For more information, please contact your band council or hamlet office, or the nearest regional office of the Department of Indian Affairs and Northern Development (DIAND). Information is also available on the DIAND Web site and the Aboriginal Youth Network Web site.

Web site: *www.inac.gc.ca/youth/index.html* (DIAND)
       www.ayn.ca (Aboriginal Youth Network)

 # First Nations Schools Co-operative Education Program

Funds are available to First Nations education authorities to establish or expand co-operative education programs in band-operated schools, federal schools, and schools administered under the James Bay and Northern Quebec Agreement.

The program provides opportunities for students in grades 7 to 13 to combine school-based learning with workplace experience. It also fosters partnerships between First Nations schools and public- and private-sector employers.

Programs are designed locally to reflect community circumstances and requirements.

For more information on how to apply and for application dates, please contact the nearest regional office of the Department of Indian Affairs and Northern Development (DIAND). Information is also available on the DIAND Web site and the Aboriginal Youth Network Web site.

Web site: *www.inac.gc.ca/youth/index.html* (DIAND)
www.ayn.ca (Aboriginal Youth Network)

🎇 Gain Experience at a National Museum

Canada's national museums have student animators, employees, interns and volunteers. In some instances, mentoring programs are also in place.

For example, the Canadian Museum of Civilization hires student animators to work with the public and for other ongoing require-ments. Student animators are hired by the Canadian Postal Museum, while at the Canadian Children's Museum young volunteers help deliver programs as well as work behind the scenes. Internships are also available in various areas of museum operations.

The National Museum of Science and Technology employs students for summer assistance on co-op programs and as interns. Many part-time jobs are available year-round in positions such as hosts and tour guides, demonstrators, and animators, or for special events and workshops.

The Canadian Museum of Nature offers weekend employment opportunities for students throughout the year and full-time oppor-tunities during the summer months. Internships, co-op assignments and volunteer opportunities are also available on an ongoing basis in educational programming, communications, fundraising, research and collections.

The National Gallery of Canada runs an academic internship program. Most internships help prepare the participant for a career in the cultural sector.

For more information, contact the national museum that you are specifically interested in assisting. Information can also be found on the Web sites of the individual museums:

- Canadian Museum of Civilization (including the Canadian Children's Museum and the Canadian Postal Museum): *www.civilization.ca/*
- National Museum of Science and Technology: *www.nmstc.ca/*
- Canadian Museum of Nature: *www.nature.ca/*
- National Gallery of Canada: *www.gallery.ca/*

In addition, the Canadian Conservation Institute, a Special Operating Agency of the Department of Canadian Heritage, offers an internship program that provides graduates of conservation or science programs with practical experience in their field of study.

For more information, visit the Institute's Web site and click on Learning Opportunities.

Web site: *www.cci-icc.gc.ca*

Geological Survey of Canada Student Assistant Program

If you are a full-time, post-secondary student specializing in geology, geophysics, geochemistry, computer science or related disciplines, and are planning to return to full-time studies in the fall, you may be interested in applying — through the Federal Student Work Experience Program — for a summer job with the Geological Survey of Canada.

Information is available from Human Resources Development Canada offices, university and college placement offices, and Public Service Commission (PSC) offices across Canada. [See the Important Addresses and Phone Numbers index for a list of PSC regional offices.] You may also contact:

Natural Resources Canada
Earth Sciences Sector
601 Booth Street, Room 100
Ottawa, ON K1A 0E8
Tel: *(613) 992-0482*
Fax: *(613) 947-1831*
E-mail: *gchiarel@nrcan.gc.ca*

🔅 House of Commons Page Programme

Each year, about 40 students are selected from high schools and community colleges or CEGEPs across Canada. They serve the House of Commons while beginning their studies at a university in the National Capital Region, and they collect friendships and memories that will last a lifetime.

Pages play a key role in the communication network on Parliament Hill. Delivering important messages and research papers to Members, linking Members to their Hill offices, and serving House officials in various capacities, House of Commons Pages are always on the go.

Professional, prompt and efficient service has become a hallmark of the House of Commons Page Programme.

For more information, ask your high-school or CEGEP guidance counsellor or contact:

House of Commons Page Programme (Recruitment)
Financial and Human Resources Services Directorate
Wellington Building, Room 538
Ottawa, ON K1A 0A6
Tel: *(613) 996-0897*
Web site: *www.parl.gc.ca/36/pp-e.htm*

If you're a youth living in Western Canada – or a small-business owner operating there – you may also be interested in the First Jobs in Science and Technology program described in the *Entrepreneurship* section of this publication.

Housing Internship Initiative for First Nations and Inuit Youth

This youth employment initiative provides work experience and on-the-job training for First Nations and Inuit youth who have an eligible sponsor. The intent of the program is to help them pursue long-term employment in the housing industry. Approved sponsors receive financial support toward the wages of First Nations or Inuit youth employed on housing-related projects.

Sponsors must be able to offer work experience and on-the-job training related to housing activities such as housing administration, construction, renovation, maintenance and client counselling. They must be located on-reserve or in an Inuit community and must be able to provide travel and accommodation costs for youth trainees required to work away from home.

To obtain additional program information and an application guide, contact your band or community housing office, call the Canada Mortgage and Housing Corporation (CMHC) office nearest you, or contact:

CMHC
Tel: *1 800 668-2642*
TTY: *1 800 309-3388*
Fax: *(613) 748-4069*
E-mail: *chic@cmhc-schl.gc.ca*
Web site: *www.cmhc-schl.gc.ca*

Information Highway Science and Entrepreneurship Camps

Information Highway Science and Entrepreneurship Camps hire youth counsellors who plan and present hands-on activities — from environmental field studies to Net-controlled robotic devices — in a fun atmosphere. Although every camp is different, all have an information highway component. Interns gain experience in business areas such as marketing and sponsorship, and improve their communication, teamwork and problem-solving skills.

These day camps are operated by non-profit groups such as science centres, museums, school boards and universities. While the camps are held during the months of July and August, youth counsellors are usually employed from May to September. Over 200 youth were hired in the first two years of the program.

For more information, please contact:

Information Highway Science and Entrepreneurship Camps
Industry Canada
155 Queen Street, 7th Floor
Ottawa, ON K1A 0H5
Tel: *(613) 993-5249*
E-mail: *mckendy.joe@ic.gc.ca*

International Trade Personnel Program

This unique funding program is designed for growing export-oriented businesses in Western Canada and young people wanting jobs in the industry. The International Trade Personnel Program provides funds for small businesses to employ eligible post-secondary graduates to help implement export marketing projects.

For more information, please contact:

Western Economic Diversification Canada
Toll-free: *1 888 338-WEST* (9378)
Web site: *www.wd.gc.ca*

Internship Programs in Film and Television Production

The Canadian Film and Television Production Association (CFTPA) National Mentorship Programs provide internship opportunities in film and television across Canada.

International Intern Program for Canadian Youth

Funded by the Department of Foreign Affairs and International Trade, this program offers on-the-job work experience to interns in both the domestic and international film and television industry.

Tel: *1 800 972-3872* (toll-free)
E-mail: *training@cftpa.ca*

Production Internship Program for Canadian Youth

Funded by Human Resources Development Canada, this program offers young people work experience and a look behind the scenes of the film and television production industry.

Tel: *1 800 290-9734* (toll-free)
E-mail: *nmp@cftpa.ca*

The CFTPA is a national non-profit trade association representing over 300 companies in Canada's film and television production industry. The Association promotes the industry by lobbying on behalf of independent producers, offering educational training programs and seminars, and distributing a regular series of publications.

Web site: *www.cftpa.ca*

 Justice Articling Program

Men and women working toward a law degree and professional accreditation can gain extensive and diverse experience with seasoned lawyers who serve as mentors providing guidance and regular feedback.

With the rotation system at the Department of Justice, students can obtain experience in advisory, litigation and policy activities. Students rotate through two to four areas of law, depending on their training and interests and on operational requirements.

Information on the Department of Justice Articling Program is available on our Web site.

For more information, contact:

Department of Justice Canada
Ottawa, ON K1A 0H8
Tel: *(613) 954-6711*
Fax: *(613) 954-3000* or *(613) 957-8381*
E-mail: *sylvie.forgues@justice.gc.ca*
Web site: *http://canada.justice.gc.ca/en/dept/ri/rec/so/artpro.html*

Library of Parliament Student Program

The Library of Parliament hires a limited number of students for clerical work — part-time during the academic year and full-time during the summer months. For the summer program, preference is given to library science or library technology students.

Information requests and applications should be addressed to:

Library of Parliament
Human Resources
Ottawa, ON K1A 0A9

Management Trainee Program

If you have a master's degree in any discipline from a recognized university, you may want to explore a career with Canada's public service in a program that is designed to train and develop individuals to become future managers. The Management Trainee Program (MTP) recruits highly talented individuals who demonstrate vision and leadership abilities, and trains these persons over a period of four to five years to help them develop the skills and knowledge required to assume middle-management positions.

Throughout the program, participants undertake a number of assignments of increasing responsibility. This provides them with the opportunity to build their management skills in a professional environment and to develop a solid understanding of the structure and processes of the Government of Canada.

If you are graduating, or have recently graduated, with a master's degree from a recognized university, you are eligible to apply.

For general information on the program, visit the MTP Web site.

Recruitment takes place in late summer/early fall of each year. At that time of year, there are three different methods for you to find out how to apply. You may:

- consult the Public Service Commission (PSC) recruitment Web site,
- visit the campus career centre at your post-secondary institution, or
- visit the nearest PSC office.

A list of our regional offices appears in the Important Addresses and Phone Numbers index.

Web site: *www.psc-cfp.gc.ca/mtp/index.htm* (MTP)
    http://jobs.gc.ca (PSC recruitment)

National Research Council Research Associateships Program

The National Research Council of Canada (NRC) offers the opportunity to break new ground with NRC researchers of international stature. Research associateships are tenable only in NRC laboratories.

Associateships are open to nationals of all countries, although preference will be given to Canadians. Applicants must have obtained a PhD in natural science or engineering, or a master's degree in an engineering field, within the last five years — or they must expect to obtain the degree before taking up the associateship.

Demonstrated ability to perform original research of high quality in the chosen field will be the main criterion used in selecting candidates and in considering term extensions.

For more information, please contact:

Resourcing Group
National Research Council of Canada
Montréal Road
Building M-58, Room W-112
Ottawa, ON K1A 0R6
Tel: *(613) 993-9134*
Fax: *(613) 990-7669*
E-mail: *ra.coordinator@nrc.ca*
Web site: *www.nrc.ca/careers*

⚡ National Research Council Summer Employment Program

Summer positions offered at most National Research Council of Canada (NRC) branches and institutes across Canada could provide you with practical career-related experience in research or in other disciplines such as library sciences, communications and marketing.

To be eligible, you must be an excellent student who is returning to full-time studies in the fall. You must also be a Canadian citizen or a permanent resident of Canada studying at a Canadian institution and have a B+ average.

Each term lasts for about 16 weeks. Salaries are based on the number of academic terms a student has completed.

Applications will be accepted via our Web site starting in mid-October. Once you have applied through the Internet, transcripts should be forwarded by mail or fax. To be considered, applications and transcripts must be received by January 31.

For more information, contact:

Summer Program Coordinator
National Research Council of Canada
Human Resources Branch
Montréal Road
Building M-58, Room W-112
Ottawa, ON K1A 0R6
Fax: *(613) 990-7669* or *(613) 941-6345*
Web site: *www.nrc.ca/careers*

 Official Language Monitor Program

This program promotes both official languages and their respective cultures. As an official language monitor, you will work in your first official language as a resource person in an educational setting. Full-time monitors travel to rural or semi-urban communities and work in schools with teachers, supplementing their educational activities. Part-time monitors do the same type of work, but they do it in urban areas while they continue their post-secondary studies.

If you are selected as a monitor, and your first language is English, you will interact with students whose first language is French. While you will receive some training in preparation for your work, you must have an excellent command of your first official language.

To be eligible, you must be a Canadian citizen and you must have been registered as a full-time student for at least one semester within the last two years. You must also have completed, at minimum, one year of post-secondary study, or a diplôme d'études collégiales in Quebec, by June of the year of your application.

The deadline for applications is February 15. **For more information**, contact the Canadian Heritage office nearest you, as listed in the Government of Canada pages of your telephone directory.

Parliamentary Tours

Each year, hundreds of thousands of visitors from across Canada and around the world are escorted through the historic halls of the Parliament Buildings.

Working in both official languages, parliamentary guides:

- greet and welcome visitors at the Centre Block and at the East Block;
- interpret Canada's political history, its legislative process, and the art and architecture of the Parliament Buildings as well as the Peace Tower and the Memorial Chamber;
- adapt the tour content to suit the needs of various groups, including international visitors, dignitaries and school groups; and

- assist and serve the parliamentarians, their staff and the general public.

Recruitment is conducted through campus student placement centres at accredited universities across Canada. **Information on the program** is available on the Parliamentary Internet Parlementaire site under Parliamentary Programs. You can also call the Library of Parliament's Information Service.

Tel: *(613) 992-4793*
Web site: *www.parl.gc.ca*

Partners in Promoting Summer Employment

Business people understand how important summer jobs are to a future career. They also recognize that today's youth are tomorrow's workers. As a partnership between the Government of Canada and local business associations, the program provides business associations with funding to hire students and to promote the hiring of students within their communities without using government wage subsidies.

For more information, contact your nearest Human Resources Development Canada (HRDC) office or HRDC Office for Students, as listed in the Government of Canada pages of your telephone directory. You can also call the Youth Info Line.

Youth Info Line: *1 800 935-5555* (toll-free)

Post-Secondary Recruitment for the Federal Public Service

The Post-Secondary Recruitment Campaign is a national initiative to recruit post-secondary graduates who possess the talent and skills required to meet the challenging demands of a career in Canada's public service. These careers offer you the opportunity to work in your field of study and to use your skills and expertise in the service of Canada.

Federal government departments and agencies are looking for specific academic backgrounds and disciplines, ranging from computer science to public administration, to meet their human resource needs. This annual Post-Secondary Recruitment Campaign generally lasts from early September to early October of each year. In addition, a winter campaign is held in January/February of each year.

If you are a new or recent graduate and are interested in a public service career with the Government of Canada, you are eligible to apply.

For more information, or to find out how to apply, consult the Public Service Commission recruitment Web site or visit the campus career centre at your post-secondary institution or the nearest office of the Public Service Commission of Canada. [See the Important Addresses and Phone Numbers index in this publication for the regional office nearest you.]

Web site: *http://jobs.gc.ca*

Royal Canadian Mounted Police Summer Student Program

A partnership with Human Resources Development Canada, this program gives students the opportunity to work alongside members of the Royal Canadian Mounted Police (RCMP) as sworn peace officers — with powers of arrest and dressed in regular uniform. Students perform a variety of duties, with the objective of gaining knowledge of and experience in the front-end operations of the criminal justice system and the RCMP.

Managed by the Crime Prevention/Victims' Services Branch, the program runs from May to September each year. The recruiting process for these positions varies depending on the division but usually starts by mid-January.

If you are interested in applying, forward your resumé by fax to the divisional recruiting office in the area in which you are seeking summer employment.

Alberta	*(780) 412-5380*
British Columbia	*(604) 264-3546*
Manitoba	*(780) 412-5381*

New Brunswick	*(506) 451-6054*
Newfoundland	*(709) 772-3140*
Northwest Territories	*(867) 669-5104*
Nova Scotia	*(902) 426-3952*
Nunavut	*(867) 979-7897*
Ontario	*(519) 645-4707*
Ottawa	*(613) 993-2404*
Prince Edward Island	*(902) 368-0357*
Quebec	*(514) 283-2169*
Saskatchewan	*(306) 780-6105*
Yukon	*(867) 393-6791*

SchoolNet Youth Employment Initiative

The SchoolNet Youth Employment Initiative provides funding for participating organizations to provide employment opportunities for unemployed and underemployed young people aged 15 to 30. These 16-week work terms develop and strengthen employability skills and ease the transition to longer-term career-related employment. The initiative supports the implementation of technology in the learning process, helps schools and public libraries use and integrate information and communications technology (ICT) effectively, and helps to ensure that learners have an opportunity to develop ICT skills.

The responsibilities of the youth hired include implementing and maintaining the technical aspects of connectivity, showing schools and libraries the basics of the Internet to increase the level of comfort and familiarity with information technology and helping them use it effectively. Past participants have an excellent rate of employment in their field of interest following their work terms — having gained multimedia and technology skills as well as experience in training and education.

For more information, please contact:

SchoolNet Youth Employment Initiative
Industry Canada
155 Queen Street, 4th Floor
Ottawa, ON K1A 0H5
Tel: *1 800 575-9200*
E-mail: *schoolnet@ic.gc.ca*
Web site: *www.schoolnet.ca/yei*

Science and Technology Internship Program – Horticultural

Through the Science and Technology Internship Program, the Horticultural Human Resource Council is creating unique partnerships with private-sector non-governmental organizations and universities. The intern is an employee of the partner.

This program provides structured work terms to unemployed or underemployed graduates in the horticultural science and technology sector. As an intern, you will have an opportunity to obtain portable skills and, in some cases, crucial first job experience in your field of specialization. Internships of up to one year in duration are available across Canada.

For more information, please contact:

Horticultural Human Resource Council – National Office & Atlantic Region
131 Kee Road
Keswick Ridge, NB E6L 1V3
Tel: *(506) 363-3310*
Fax: *(506) 363-8991*
E-mail: *hort@nbnet.nb.ca*

Horticultural Human Resource Council – BC Region
203A-15225 104th Avenue
Surrey, BC V3R 6Y8
Tel: *(604) 588-1958*
Fax: *(604) 588-1010*
E-mail: *bchort@iceonline.com*

Institut québécois des ressources humaines en horticulture
570 boul Roland Therrien, bureau 206
Longueuil, QC J4H 3V9
Tel: *(450) 679-8810*
Fax: *(450) 679-2214*
E-mail: *iqrhh@iqrhh.qc.ca*

Horticultural Human Resource Council – Ontario Region
7856 Fifth Line South, RR #4 Station Main
Milton, ON L9T 2X8
Tel: *(905) 875-1805*
Fax: *(905) 875-3942*
E-mail: *landscapeontario@spectranet.ca*

Science and Technology Internship Program (Natural Resources Canada)

Sponsored by Natural Resources Canada (NRCan), this internship program provides an opportunity for recent graduates in science, engineering or business to gain relevant and meaningful work experience. Activities may include all aspects of the innovation or technology process as well as commercial business applications.

Under the direction of experienced scientists, interns work on cutting-edge research and development projects with NRCan partners committed to bringing research to commercial application. The intern is an employee of the partner.

Interested youth should market themselves to eligible partners of NRCan (e.g., universities, private companies, non-federal government organizations) as possible candidates for internships under this program. A partner may then contact NRCan with an internship proposal. Existing partnerships are targeted to provide internship opportunities that are within the mandate of the Department.

Fifty internships of up to one year in duration are available across Canada every year.

For more information, please contact:

Natural Resources Canada
580 Booth Street, C2, 6th Floor
Ottawa, ON K1A 0E4
Tel: *(613) 995-6275*
Fax: *(613) 947-4117*
E-mail: *gmasse@nrcan.gc.ca*
Web site: *www.nrcan.gc.ca/css/hrsb/intern-e.htm*

Want to find out more about SchoolNet?
Turn to the *Skills Development and Learning Opportunities* section of this publication.

Science and Technology Internship Program with SMEs

Offered by the National Research Council of Canada (NRC) through its Industrial Research Assistance Program (IRAP), this program is a Youth Employment Strategy initiative.

The program offers six-month internships in small- and medium-sized enterprises (SMEs) anywhere in Canada. If you are a recent graduate in science, engineering, technology, finance, administration, marketing or liberal arts and are unemployed or underemployed, you may be eligible. The Science and Technology Internship Program with SMEs will give you valuable work experience that will help open doors to future employment.

For more information, call the Youth Info Line or visit the NRC IRAP Web site. To apply, visit the Campus WorkLink Web site (formerly known as the National Graduate Register).

Youth Info Line: *1 800 935-5555* (toll-free)
Web site: *www.nrc.ca/irap* (NRC IRAP)
Web site: www.*campusworklink.com* (Campus WorkLink)

Science and Technology Internships in Apparel Program

Are you a college or university graduate seeking employment and a career in a fast-paced, dynamic industry? The Science and Technology Internship in Apparel Program (STIAP) helps apparel manufacturers build their technical capacity while providing interns with employment experience and, hopefully, long-term positions.

STIAP offers a wage subsidy of up to $8000 per internship to apparel manufacturers who hire unemployed or underemployed post-secondary graduates under 30 years of age. Internships range from six months to one year. Among others, eligible positions include:

- information technology applications (e.g., marker making, e-commerce);
- industrial and mechanical engineering;
- production machinery repair and maintenance;
- production supervision and management (or assistant);

- quality assurance (e.g., fabric testing);
- design, using Computer Aided Design (CAD) stations; and
- accounting, with a view to more accurate costing of products/lines.

You can take advantage of this exciting opportunity by informing a potential employer, who is an apparel manufacturer, about the program and obtaining an application form from the Apparel Human Resources Council. Only a limited number of subsidies are available, so act quickly!

For more information, contact:

Apparel Human Resources Council
130 Slater Street, Suite 1050
Ottawa, ON K1P 6E2
Tel: *(613) 567-4144*
Fax: *(613) 567-4147*
E-mail: *stiap@apparel-hrc.org*
Web site: *www.apparel-hrc.org*

Science and Technology Youth Internships Program

Position yourself for a future in cutting-edge marine and oceanic science. Through its Science and Technology Youth Internships Program, Fisheries and Oceans Canada has created unique partnerships with the private sector, non-governmental organizations and universities. These internships will appeal to graduates with a background in marine sciences, environmental studies, engineering, informatics, marketing or similar fields.

As an intern, you'll have a wide choice of short-term work placements in marine and oceanic research, which has never been more challenging or interesting. Each internship will be an intensive learning experience. Through practical day-to-day experience, you'll learn many of the communication, problem-solving and project management skills you'll need when seeking further employment in the scientific community. Interns may work in partners' facilities, departmental laboratories or field settings.

The quickest way to apply is through the Campus Worklink Web site. **For more information** on the program, visit Fisheries and Oceans Canada's Web site. For information on the full range of Government of Canada youth employment programs, call the Youth Info Line.

Youth Info Line: *1 800 935-5555* (toll-free)
Web site: *www.campusworklink.com* (Campus WorkLink)
Web site: *www.dfo-mpo.gc.ca/ssip/* (Fisheries and Oceans Canada)

Science Collaborative Research Internships Program

Offered by the National Research Council of Canada (NRC) through its Industrial Research Assistance Program (IRAP), this program is a Youth Employment Strategy initiative.

The program offers six-month internships in small- and medium-sized Canadian enterprises involved in collaborative research with NRC or the Communications Research Centre. If you are a recent graduate in science, engineering, technology, finance, administration or marketing and are unemployed or underemployed, you may be eligible. The Science Collaborative Research Internships Program will give you valuable work experience that will help open doors to future employment.

For more information, call the Youth Info Line or visit the NRC IRAP Web site. To apply, visit the Campus WorkLink Web site (formerly known as the National Graduate Register).

Youth Info Line: *1 800 935-5555* (toll-free)
Web site: *www.nrc.ca/irap* (NRC IRAP)
Web site: www.*campusworklink.com* (Campus WorkLink)

 **Senate Page Program**

The Senate Page Program provides a great opportunity for young Canadians to further their knowledge of Canadian parliamentary affairs. Pages get the chance to participate in a variety of activities associated with the legislative process of Canada's Parliament. Each year, 15 university students from all over Canada are chosen as Senate pages.

To be eligible, you must:

- be a full-time student enrolled in one of the universities in the National Capital Region;
- be attending the first, second, third or fourth year of your *first* undergraduate degree in September of the following year (unless you have obtained a degree);
- not have former experience as a page on Parliament Hill;
- be bilingual at level AAB/AAB (minimum proficiency for reading and writing, and intermediate proficiency for oral interaction in both official languages); and
- be a Canadian citizen or a permanent resident.

Pages are paid $8329 in 26 equal instalments. Upon satisfactory completion of their contract, they receive an additional $1200. Pages are required to work a minimum of 15 hours a week when the Senate and Committees are sitting. Once the school year is completed, pages may work up to 35 hours per week for a maximum of 700 and a minimum of 500 hours annually.

If you are interested in participating in the Senate Page Program, please send us your resumé. Applications will be placed in the inventory and candidates will be notified during the next selection process.

For more information, contact:

Human Resources Advisor
Services to Senators & Official Languages
Human Resources Directorate
Parliament Buildings
The Senate of Canada
Ottawa, ON K1N 0A4
Tel: *(613) 992-8042*
Toll-free: *1 800 267-7362*
Fax: *(613) 992-1995*
E-mail: *bernir@sen.parl.gc.ca*

 Shad Valley Summer Program

The National Research Council of Canada (NRC) has joined the
Canadian Advanced Technology Association in supporting the
award-winning Shad Valley summer program for senior high-school
students.

Shad Valley is run by Shad International — an independent organization based in Waterloo, Ontario that collaborates with education,
business and other organizations to promote the advancement of
the scientific, technological and entrepreneurial capabilities of
Canadian youth.

Shad Valley takes place on eight university campuses in Canada
during the month of July. Each university hosts about 50 students
for a series of challenging lectures, workshops, labs and seminars.
Most participants round out their Shad experience with a five-week
work term with a sponsoring company or organization.

Participants cover tuition and related fees by fundraising and seeking support from program sponsors. As a major sponsor, NRC has
first access to the pool of Shad participants for work terms in its
research institutes from coast-to-coast.

You are eligible if you are a senior high-school student and a Canadian citizen or a permanent resident of Canada. Applications are available from high schools or directly from Shad International.

For more information, contact:

Shad International
8 Young Street East
Waterloo, ON N2J 2L3
Tel: *(519) 884-8844*
Fax: *(519) 884-8191*
E-mail: *info@shad.ca*
Web site: *www.nrc.ca/careers*

Social Assistance Work Opportunities Program

Residents on First Nations reserves who are eligible for social assistance and who volunteer to take part can gain valuable training and work experience by participating in projects funded through this program.

First Nations can transfer social assistance funds to support employment and training projects that provide work experience to unemployed people in the community.

The projects are designed to improve chances for employment and to produce goods and services to benefit the community. Social assistance funds must be combined with funding from other sources and can be used for capital, wages or training allowances. Participating social assistance recipients must be provided with wages/living allowances that are at least equal to the benefits they would have received by remaining on social assistance.

Only bands or organizations responsible to a chief and council may apply to sponsor a project. Applications must come from the Department of Indian Affairs and Northern Development (DIAND) regional office.

For more details and a copy of the DIAND Social Assistance Program Manual, please contact the DIAND office in your region.

🌀 Software Internships 2000

Software Internships 2000 is a program that helps recent university and college graduates, as well as graduates of privately operated information technology (IT) training schools, obtain entry-level positions with Canadian IT employers through internships.

Graduates must be under the age of 30 and eligible to work in Canada, and they must have graduated within four years of having started the internship.

Eligible organizations must be Canadian-owned and have less than 200 employees, and they must be active in the IT sector. The job opportunities for interns must be software-skills related.

Participating organizations are provided with wage subsidies of up to $6000. Graduates who have the requisite computer skills and training are matched with participating organizations through Campus WorkLink. [See the Campus WorkLink listing in the *Job-Search Tools* section of this publication.]

Since its launch in 1998, this program has provided meaningful work experience, in a software marketing, sales, customer service or technician role, for over 160 unemployed or underemployed IT graduates.

For more information, contact:

Software Human Resource Council
30 Metcalfe Street, Suite 400
Ottawa, ON K1P 5L4
Tel: *(613) 237-8551*
Fax: *(613) 230-3490*
E-mail: *info@shrc.ca*
Web site: *www.shrc.ca*

Student Connection Program

Funded through the Youth Employment Strategy, the Student Connection Program is an Industry Canada initiative that hires university and college students as Student Business Advisors. Assisting small- and medium-sized businesses, these specially trained students provide customized, hands-on Internet and electronic commerce training.

Since the program began in 1996, over 3000 students and 64 000 business people have benefited from its services. Students gain valuable on-the-job work experience while financing their education.

Students or businesses **interested in learning more** about the Student Connection Program should call toll-free or visit the Web site.

Tel: *1 888 807-7777*
Web site: *www.scp-ebb.com*

Student Customs Officer Program

Positions are available at Customs Border Services offices across Canada. On successful completion of the customs inspector test, and after appropriate training, students perform certain customs inspector functions under the supervision of senior customs staff. These duties include clearing travellers, examining baggage and goods, and performing other customs-related activities. Shift work is often required.

To apply, you must be at least 16 years of age, currently attending a post-secondary institution on a full-time basis and registered with the Public Service Commission of Canada (PSC) under the Federal Student Work Experience Program (FSWEP). [See the FSWEP listing in this section.] Preference may be given to students in a field related to the job such as criminology, law and security, law enforcement or business administration.

Applications can be made year-round at PSC offices across Canada. [See the Important Addresses and Phone Numbers index in this publication for the office nearest you.]

 **Student Summer Job Action**

The Student Summer Job Action (SSJA) component of Canada's Youth Employment Strategy creates summer work experiences for secondary and post-secondary students. A partnership program with various groups in the private and not-for-profit sectors, SSJA helps students gain work experience through wage subsidies to employers, interest-free loans to students, promotional activities and information.

If you are a secondary or post-secondary student returning to full-time studies in the fall, and you are legally entitled to work in Canada, you may be eligible to participate in the program.

For more information, contact your local Human Resources Development Canada Office for Students during summer months or your local Human Resources Development Canada office at other times. These are both listed in the Government of Canada pages of your telephone directory. You can also call the Youth Info Line or browse the Youth Resource Network of Canada Web site.

Youth Info Line: *1 800 935-5555* (toll-free)
Web site: *www.youth.gc.ca* (Youth Resource Network of Canada)

 **Summer Career Placements**

Summer Career Placements (SCP) provides wage subsidies to not-for-profit organizations and private- and public-sector businesses to create career-related summer work experiences for students. The program is a component of Student Summer Job Action, which is part of Canada's Youth Employment Strategy.

Application forms for employers wishing **to apply for** an SCP subsidy can be obtained by contacting your local Human Resources Development Canada office, as listed in the Government of Canada section of your telephone directory, or by calling the Youth Info Line.

Youth Info Line: *1 800 935-5555* (toll-free)

Technology First Work Placement Service

This national, not-for-profit placement service has been established to help graduate technicians and technologists get valuable first work experience with small- to medium-sized companies that need trained technical staff. Administered by the Canadian Technology Human Resources Board (CTHRB), the Technology First Work Placement Service matches graduates with prospective employers. Participants get the experience they need to begin working in their field of study, while companies get access to a pool of highly trained and motivated employees from across Canada.

Graduates are placed with companies that are willing to hire technicians or technologists for paid work terms of between 6 and 12 months. During their work term, graduates are hosted by a certified engineering technologist — who mentors and helps the participant develop an understanding of the realities of the workplace and the profession. There are no obligations on the part of the employer once the work term is over. However, if a company wants to hire a graduate full-time, it is free to do so.

For more information, please call the CTHRB. To register, visit the Technology First Work Placement Service Web site.

Canadian Technology Human Resources Board
Tel: *1 800 216-9462* (toll-free)
Web site: *www.cthrb.ca/1tech/*

Textile Management Internship Program

Are you an engineering, science or technology graduate under 30 years of age? You may be interested in our one-year Textile Management Internship Program (TMIP) — a program with 100% industry placement and excellent starting and long-range salaries!

TMIP is a unique and innovative post-graduate program developed and managed by the Textiles Human Resources Council. Since the majority of textile firms are located in Quebec and Ontario, preference will be given to candidates who can fluently communicate in both of Canada's official languages.

The program is delivered by McMaster University's Michael G. DeGroote School of Business and the Faculty of Engineering Technology at Mohawk College, both located in Hamilton, Ontario, and North Carolina State University's world-renowned College of Textiles located in Raleigh, North Carolina.

If you are looking for a challenging and rewarding career, send your resumé — qualified applicants will be sent an application package — or contact the Council **for more information**.

Textile Management Internship Program
Textiles Human Resources Council
66 Slater Street, Suite 1720
Ottawa, ON K1P 5H1
Tel: *(613) 230-7217* ext. 310
E-mail: *shirley.mckey.thrc@sympatico.ca*
Web site: *www3.sympatico.ca/thrc*

 Tourism Careers for Youth

This national sector-based youth internship program assists young people between the ages of 18 and 29 with the transition from school to work and prepares them for the workforce.

The program offers a mix of classroom and on-the-job training that provides young people with the skills, knowledge, attitudes and experience required for long-term employment in tourism — the world's fastest growing industry. Young people involved in the program enjoy three weeks of pre-employment classroom training, career planning and employability skills training prior to their job placement.

As a result of strong industry support, these young people are then hired for six months in entry-level tourism occupations. Workplace supervisors, who have completed a two-day train-the-trainer workshop, provide their new employees with a minimum of 90 hours of standards-based technical skills training using national workbooks and trainers'guides.

For more information, contact:

Canadian Tourism Human Resources Council
170 Laurier Avenue West, Suite 1104
Ottawa, ON K1P 5V5
Tel: *(613) 231-6949*
Fax: *(613) 231-6853*
E-mail: *cthrc@cthrc.ca*
Web site: *www.cthrc.ca*

Women in Engineering and Science Program

Work with world-class researchers in top facilities as part of the National Research Council of Canada (NRC) Women in Engineering and Science (WES) Program. This unique program encourages greater participation of women in the under-represented fields of engineering, science and mathematics.

Once accepted into WES, you'll become a part-time employee for two years — with the possibility of a third year. As you continue your studies, you'll work in NRC laboratories on research projects during the summer or during your co-op work terms. You will be paid a salary. Throughout your tenure in the WES Program, you'll team up with an NRC scientist or engineer. This mentor will provide you with the guidance and direction necessary for you to define and reach your goals.

To be eligible, you must be a Canadian citizen or permanent resident currently attending a Canadian university and have a high academic standing. If you reside in the province of Quebec and have completed two years of CEGEP, you must be enrolled full-time in an undergraduate physics, science, engineering or mathematics university program; if you have not completed two years of CEGEP, you must be enrolled full-time in your second year of an undergraduate program in science, engineering or mathematics by October 15.

Application forms may be obtained from, and should be returned to, your university awards office or campus contact. Each university in Canada can submit the names of up to three nominees to be considered for WES.

For further information, contact:

Resourcing Group
National Research Council of Canada
Montréal Road
Building M-58, Room W-112
Ottawa, ON K1A 0R6
Tel: *(613) 993-9134*
Fax: *(613) 990-7669*
E-mail: *wes.coordinator@nrc.ca*
Web site: *www.nrc.ca/careers*

 Young Canada Works

As part of the Government of Canada's Youth Employment Strategy, and in partnership with the private sector and various national and community organizations, Young Canada Works is a Department of Canadian Heritage program that provides summer employment and internship opportunities to Canadian youth.

Young Canada Works in Both Official Languages

Take your language and academic skills out of the classroom and into the workforce. Under the language component of Young Canada Works, summer jobs provide hands-on work experience to fine-tune skills already acquired in school. The work and/or work environment will be in your second official language and in a field related to your studies.

Work functions vary greatly, but employment in the following disciplines is likely to be in demand:

- business administration (especially small business management)
- media and communications
- heritage and cultural tourism
- cultural industries

You can apply on-line at the Campus WorkLink Web site (formerly the National Graduate Register). Employers conduct on-line searches at this site to select participants.

Young Canada Works in Both Official Languages
Toll-free: *1 800 935-5555* (Youth Info Line)

Web site: *www.pch.gc.ca/ycw-jct/* (Canadian Heritage)
         www.campusworklink.com/ (Campus WorkLink)

Young Canada Works in Heritage Institutions

Explore career choices and learn about Canada's history and heritage while helping museums, archives, libraries and other heritage organizations across Canada in their efforts to reflect and showcase Canada to Canadians. These summer jobs in heritage institutions provide you with hands-on work experience that lasts between 8 and 12 weeks.

Work functions vary greatly, and you can gain experience in a number of areas that will help facilitate career choices: working with exhibits and heritage collections, developing new media products and Web sites, writing and editing, animating children's summer programs, hosting or performing in heritage programs, marketing, conservation or restoration, research, and many other opportunities.

You are eligible to apply if you are a student 16 to 30 years of age (recent graduates can also apply). Some jobs may require specific skills and basic knowledge of museums, archives, library science, etc.

You can apply on-line at the Campus WorkLink Web site (formerly the National Graduate Register). Employers conduct on-line searches at this site to select participants.

Young Canada Works in Heritage Institutions
Toll-free: *1 800 935-5555* (Youth Info Line)
Web site: *www.pch.gc.ca/ycw-jct/* (Canadian Heritage)
         www.campusworklink.com/ (Campus WorkLink)

Young Canada Works in National Parks and National Historic Sites

Located at selected national parks and national historic sites across Canada, these summer employment opportunities focus on at least two disciplines such as:

- history
- tourism
- client services and resource management
- environmental work

To be eligible, you should be between 16 and 18 years of age and a full-time student. (A few supervisory positions are available for more experienced individuals.)

If you are interested, you should complete the Federal Student Work Experience Program (FSWEP) application form (before May 3) available from the Public Service Commission of Canada or local Human Resources Development Canada offices. [See the FSWEP listing earlier in this section.]

Young Canada Works in National Parks and National Historic Sites
Toll-free: *1 800 935-5555* (Youth Info Line)
Web site: *www.pch.gc.ca/ycw-jct/* (Canadian Heritage)

Young Canada Works for Aboriginal Urban Youth

This component of Young Canada Works is for Aboriginal youth living in urban centres served by Aboriginal Friendship Centres. Aboriginal youth who are eligible are high-school students, post-secondary students or graduates, unemployed, and between the ages of 16 and 24.

Participants may be asked to develop, supervise or manage activities within the Friendship Centres. These activities can include:

- youth and children's programs
- cultural and recreation projects
- various counselling programs

Interested Aboriginal youth can apply directly on the Internet by keying in the necessary information at the Campus WorkLink Web site or by sending applications to their local Aboriginal Friendship Centre.

Young Canada Works for Aboriginal Urban Youth
Toll-free: *1 800 935-5555* (Youth Info Line)
Web site: *www.pch.gc.ca/ycw-jct/* (Canadian Heritage)
        www.campusworklink.com (Campus WorkLink)

National Association of Friendship Centres
275 MacLaren Street
Ottawa, ON K2P 0L9
Tel: *(613) 563-4844*
Fax: *(613) 594-3428*
E-mail: *auysop@nafc-aboriginal.com*
Web site: *www.auysop.com*

Young Canada Works in Science and Technology

This component of Young Canada Works offers internship opportunities through partnerships between the Department of Canadian
Heritage and other public and non-profit organizations in the cultural and heritage sector. Graduates in science or technology from
across Canada have the opportunity to play a key role in expanding
new and emerging technologies and to apply their skills in new
ways while improving their longer-term job prospects.

Under this component, unemployed or underemployed university
and college graduates work in cultural and heritage organizations
— such as museums, archives and libraries — or in organizations
that are involved in theatre, dance, music, publishing, film and
video, multimedia or other similar areas within the cultural and heritage sectors.

Participants are under the age of 30. Internships last from 4 to 12
months and are in the areas of technology and/or applied scientific
research.

You can apply on-line at the Campus WorkLink Web site (formerly
the National Graduate Register). Employers conduct on-line searches
at this site to select participants.

Young Canada Works in Science and Technology
Toll-free: *1 800 935-5555* (Youth Info Line)
Web site: *www.pch.gc.ca/ycw-jct/* (Canadian Heritage)
        www.campusworklink.com/ (Campus WorkLink)

Young Canada Works Internationally

This component of Young Canada Works provides young Canadians with international work experience related to their careers. Internships are provided through partnership agreements between the Department of Canadian Heritage and other private and non-governmental organizations.

Unemployed or underemployed university and college graduates can gain experience internationally in their fields of expertise — experience that will help their entry into the workforce. They also have the opportunity to raise Canada's economic and cultural profile internationally.

Participants are under the age of 30. Internships last from 6 to 12 months, with placements in participating heritage, cultural, and second-language-based institutions and organizations as well as in private-sector companies.

You can apply on-line at the Campus WorkLink Web site (formerly the National Graduate Register). Employers conduct on-line searches at this site to select participants.

Young Canada Works Internationally
Toll-free: *1 800 935-5555* (Youth Info Line)
Web site: *www.pch.gc.ca/ycw-jct/* (Canadian Heritage)
         www.campusworklink.com/ (Campus WorkLink)

Volunteering is an ideal way to get work experience and build on your current skills! Check out the Volunteer Opportunities Exchange listing in the *Job-Search Tools* section of this publication.

Youth Internship Canada

Youth Internship Canada provides funding to employers who create meaningful work experience for unemployed and underemployed youth. Internships enable young people to gain valuable work experience in their local labour market, in key areas such as science and technology, and in international trade and development.

You are eligible to apply if you are a young person (up to 30), unemployed or underemployed, out of school and legally entitled to work in Canada.

To find out what projects are available in your area, contact your nearest Human Resources Development Canada office, as listed in the Government of Canada pages of your telephone directory.

Youth Internship Program

The Canadian seafood processing industry is searching for new graduates who can adapt to its rapidly changing environment. If you are a college or university graduate under the age of 30, currently unemployed or underemployed and looking for an interesting career, this program is for you. The purpose is to give companies the chance to recruit highly educated new graduates and to give interns the opportunity to combine their education with relevant work experience with a view to long-term employment.

All Canadian companies and organizations in seafood processing are eligible to receive up to $8000 per intern. Funding may be available for up to one full year of employment. Some eligible positions would include work on the development of a Quality Management Program, food science and safety technology, food inspection, sanitation supervision, and accounting.

Take advantage of this program by informing your potential seafood processing employer of its many advantages. Funding is limited, so act soon!

To request an application form or further information, please contact:

National Seafood Sector Council
85 Albert Street, Suite 1505
Ottawa, ON K1P 6A4
Tel: *(613) 782-2391*
Fax: *(613) 782-2386*
E-mail: *hstronach@nssc.ca*
Web site: *www.nssc.ca*

Youth Service Canada

Are you a young person (up to 30), out of school, unemployed and legally entitled to work in Canada?

Youth Service Canada provides funding to organizations that create community service projects for youth who are at greatest risk of unemployment. The aim is to help young people develop the life skills and work experience they need to participate in today's labour market. As part of a team, you can gain valuable job and life skills while strengthening your sense of accomplishment through service to your community and country.

For more information, contact your local Human Resources Development Canada office.

Youth Service Canada Aboriginal Best Practices

This booklet was developed to provide Aboriginal youth project coordinators, community organizations and leaders with information on the many innovative Youth Service Canada projects. The intent is to encourage groups to take up the challenge of community service and community building and to facilitate the development of quality Aboriginal project proposals. (Cat. No. Y-206-08-97E)

Youth Service Canada: A Close Up Look at YSC

This eight-page booklet describes what YSC is, lists its priority areas and defines YSC projects in the context of community service activities. YSC participants describe how project experience is making a difference for individuals and communities. (Cat. No. Y-169-05-95)

Youth Service Canada Best Practices and Success Stories

This booklet is designed to help young people, project coordinators, everyday citizens and local community workers understand what youth service is all about. It contains an outline of the key ingredients that are necessary to create and maintain a good project, and includes a series of examples of innovative projects. (Cat. No. Y-194-09-96)

These booklets are available from:

Human Resources Development Canada
Public Enquiries Centre
140 Promenade du Portage
Hull, QC K1A 0J9
Fax: *(819) 953-7260*

Work Experience Opportunities – International

Association internationale des étudiants en sciences économiques et commerciales

The Association internationale des étudiants en sciences économiques et commerciales (AIESEC) is a student-run trade- and business-oriented international exchange program that places university students in developing countries for up to 18 months.

Participants gain valuable knowledge and experience in trade, business development and leadership, as well as in providing technical assistance in management and institution building and in conducting export missions.

The Canadian International Development Agency helps fund this program.

More information is available from:

Association internationale des étudiants en sciences économiques et commerciales
8 King Street East, Suite 208
Toronto, ON M5C 1B5
Tel: *(416) 368-1001*
Web site: *www.ca.aiesec.org*

Association of Canadian Community Colleges

The Association of Canadian Community Colleges is involved in a program to place students in developing countries for a six-month period. The students work with their counterparts in technical trades and small businesses.

The Canadian International Development Agency supports this initiative through projects financed within the Canadian College Partnership Program.

More information is available from:

Association of Canadian Community Colleges
1223 Michael Street North, Suite 200
Ottawa, ON K1J 7T2
Tel: *(613) 746-2222*
Fax: *(613) 746-6721*
Web site: *www.accc.ca*

Association Québec-France

Sponsored by the Quebec and French governments, the Association Québec-France and the Association France-Québec offer two types of cultural exchange:

- Wine harvest in France — an 8- to 10-day work permit is issued to approximately 200 young Quebec residents for harvest work; food and lodging are provided in most cases; and

- Summer employment — municipal governments in France and Quebec exchange students for summer work (6 to 8 weeks); monitors are exchanged for summer vacation camps and work camps; food and lodging are not generally provided.

To participate, you must be between 18 and 30 years of age (18 to 35 for the wine harvest), a resident of Quebec, a member of the Association ($25 membership fee), and a student. There is also a $20 program registration fee.

Registration runs from mid-January to the end of March. Depending on the program selected, there may be an amount payable for a reception and one night's accommodation in Paris.

For more information, contact:

Association Québec-France
9 Place Royale
Québec City, QC G1K 4G2
Tel: *(418) 643-1616*
Fax: *(418) 643-3053*
E-mail: *assquefr@quebectel.com*

Canada–Austria Young Workers' Exchange Program

If you are a Canadian between 18 and 30 years of age and have a post-secondary diploma or certificate from a teaching institution in the fields of tourism, agriculture or forestry, you may be interested in gaining some valuable experience working in Austria. (In some cases, the authorities of both participating countries can raise the maximum age to 35 years.)

This exchange program allows you to work in Austria for a period of six months. To be eligible, you must be a resident of Canada and have a Canadian passport that is valid for a period of three months beyond the termination of your practical training in Austria. You must also have a round-trip airplane ticket and enough funds to meet your needs during the first part of your stay. If accepted, you should also be prepared to undergo a medical examination before starting your training — if this is required by law for the activity in question — as well as pay a visa or a program participation fee.

For more information, contact:

Embassy of the Republic of Austria
445 Wilbrod Street
Ottawa, ON K1N 6M7
Tel: *(613) 789-1444*
Fax: *(613) 789-3431*

If working overseas interests you, you'll want to check out the Young Canada Works listing in the *Work Experience Opportunities* section of this publication — there's a Young Canada Works Internationally component. And if you're interested in film and television production, take a look at the Internship Programs in Film and Television Production listing in the same section.

Canada–European Community Program for Co-operation in Higher Education and Training

This program promotes student mobility through academic placements in post-secondary institutions in Europe for a minimum of one semester. Student work placement is also possible.

In Canada, the program is funded by Human Resources Development Canada and administered jointly with the Department of Foreign Affairs and International Trade. Projects are undertaken by a consortium of universities, colleges and technical institutions. Participating students do not apply directly but are selected by the post-secondary institutions involved in a project under the program.

For more information, contact:

Learning and Literacy Directorate
Human Resources Development Canada
Hull, QC K1A 0M5
Tel: *(819) 997-3362*
Fax: *(819) 953-5954*
E-mail: *tom.mccloskey@hrdc-drhc.gc.ca*
Web site: *www.hrdc-drhc.gc.ca*

Canada–France Young Workers' Exchange Program

If you are a Canadian between 18 and 35 years of age and have a university degree, a working knowledge of French and one year of relevant work experience, you may be interested in a work exchange in France.

The program allows you to work in France for 12 to 18 months in an area that is related to your field of study. You will have the opportunity to gain professional experience and to learn about the values and culture of France. Candidates are responsible for their own travel and living expenses. Work permits are required, and getting one takes up to three months after the job offer is made.

Applications are accepted throughout the year but should be made at least a few months before the desired departure date.

A fact sheet and application form are available from:

Embassy of France
42 Sussex Drive
Ottawa, ON K1M 2C9
Tel: *(613) 562-3750*
Fax: *(613) 562-3704*

Canada–Germany Young Workers' Exchange Program

Are you a Canadian between 18 and 30 years of age? Do you have a post-secondary degree or diploma in industry, commerce, science or technology, a working knowledge of German and at least one year of work experience directly related to your field of study? If so, you may be interested in gaining some valuable experience working in Germany.

The program allows you to work in Germany for 6 to 18 months in an area that is related to your field of study. You will have the opportunity to acquire new skills while gaining a better appreciation of the values and culture of Germany. The German government will do a job search on your behalf but you should also attempt to find a job on your own. You are responsible for your own travel and living expenses.

Applications are accepted year-round.

For more information and an application form, contact:

Ms Regina Mittner
Embassy of the Federal Republic of Germany
1 Waverley Street
Ottawa, ON K2P 0T8
Tel: *(613) 232-1101*
Fax: *(613) 594-9330*
Web site: *www.GermanEmbassyOttawa.org*

Consulate General of the Federal Republic of Germany
77 Admiral Road
Toronto, ON M5R 2L4
Tel: *(416) 925-2813/2814/2815*
Fax: *(416) 925-2818*

Consulate General of the Federal Republic of Germany
1250 René-Lévesque Blvd. West
41st Floor, Marathon Building
Montréal, QC H3B 4W8
Tel: *(514) 931-2277*
Fax: *(514) 931-7239*

Consulate General of the Federal Republic of Germany
World Trade Centre
999 Canada Place, Suite 704
Vancouver, BC V6C 3E1
Tel: *(604) 684-8377*
Fax: *(604) 684-8334*

 # Canada–Netherlands Young Workers' Exchange Program

If you are a Canadian citizen or permanent resident who has graduated from a post-secondary institution within the last year and have a written job offer from an employer in the Netherlands, you may be eligible for the Workers' Exchange Program with the Netherlands.

The program offers young Canadians the opportunity to experience life in the Netherlands while engaging in temporary (4 to 12 months) career-related employment. Areas of interest vary and include industry, commerce, science and technology, tourism, agriculture, and horticulture.

Applications are accepted throughout the year but should be made at least a few months before the desired departure date.

To obtain an information brochure and more information, contact:

Stichting Uitwisseling
Attention: Rosemieke van de Meerendonk
24 Goulding Crescent
Kanata, ON K2K 2N9
Tel: *(613) 599-6316*
Fax: *(613) 599-9397*
Web site: *www.uitwisseling.nl*

Canada–Switzerland Young Workers' Exchange Program

Canadians 18 to 30 years of age who have a knowledge of German, French or Italian and a university degree, a post-secondary diploma, or a certificate from an institute of technology or an equivalent educational institution are eligible. You must also have a minimum of one year of work experience directly related to your academic degree or diploma and a written job offer from a company in Switzerland.

This program permits Canadians to engage in temporary (4 to 18 months) career-related employment while gaining professional experience and learning about new cultures.

You are responsible for your own travel and living expenses. Applications should be submitted at least six months before your desired departure date.

Information and application forms are available from:

International Youth Experience
12 Laval Street
Aylmer, QC J9H 1C5
Tel: *(819) 684-9212*
Fax: *(819) 684-5630*
E-mail: *j.larochelle@experience.qc.ca*
Web site: *www.experience.qc.ca*

Canada World Youth

The Canada World Youth program allows Canadian youths under the age of 30 to learn about international developing countries as well as Central and Eastern Europe.

The program involves a reciprocal student exchange with partici-pating countries. While abroad and in Canada, youths work for voluntary-sector organizations for three to six months.

The Canadian International Development Agency helps fund this program.

More information is available from:

Canada World Youth
2330 Notre-Dame Street West, 3rd Floor
Montréal, QC H3J 1N4
Tel: *(514) 931-3526*
Toll-free: *1 800 605-3526*
Web site: *www.cwy-jcm.org*

Canada World Youth — Apprenticeship Program

Canada World Youth operates an apprenticeship program that places students 17 to 20 years of age in developing countries and Eastern Europe for six to eight months.

Participants get hands-on experience in development. The program involves a reciprocal student exchange with participating countries.

The Canadian International Development Agency helps fund this program.

More information is available from:

Canada World Youth
2330 Notre-Dame Street West, 3rd Floor
Montréal, QC H3J 1N4
Tel: *(514) 931-3526*
Toll-free: *1 800 605-3526*
Web site: *www.cwy-jcm.org*

Canadian Crossroads International

This organization places specially skilled Canadian youths between the ages of 18 and 30 in developing countries for four to six months to work on community projects in health, education and community development.

The program includes five weeks of intensive community work on their return to Canada. The Canadian International Development Agency helps fund this program.

More information is available from:

Canadian Crossroads International
31 Madison Avenue
Toronto, ON M5R 2S2
Tel: *(416) 967-0801*
Fax: *(416) 967-9078*
E-mail: *cci@crossroads-carrefour.ca*
Web site: *www.crossroads-carrefour.ca*

Capilano College

The Capilano Asia Pacific Management Co-operative Program/Canada-Association of South-East Asian Nations (APMCP/CANASEAN) exchange program provides young Canadians with an opportunity to gain international knowledge and management experience in an intercultural context.

The goal of this program is to create a close-knit network of Canadian managers who will develop Canada's enterprise and relations in Asia. They will also assist in building local institutions, where possible, and in private-sector development in developing countries.

APMCP sends young Canadian post-graduate students overseas for a practicum in affiliation with private- and public-sector firms as well as with non-governmental organizations seeking to strengthen networking links between Canada and Asia. CANASEAN brings up-and-coming ASEAN managers and executives to Canada for four months for workshops, seminars, field trips and practicums.

More information is available from:

Capilano College
2055 Purcell Way
North Vancouver, BC V7J 3H5
Tel: *(604) 984-4981*
Fax: *(604) 984-4992*
E-mail: *apmcp@capcollege.bc.ca*
Web site: *www.capcollege.bc.ca/apmcp*

⚡ Carrefour de solidarité internationale

Carrefour de solidarité internationale sends youths between 18 and 30 years of age to countries in Africa and Latin America for two months to participate in work and intercultural projects.

The Canadian International Development Agency helps fund this program.

More information is available from:

Carrefour de solidarité internationale
555 Short Street
Sherbrooke, QC   J1H 2E6
Tel: *(819) 566-8595*
E-mail: *info@csisher.com*
Web site: *www.csisher.com*

⚡ Centre canadien d'étude et de coopération internationale

The Centre canadien d'étude et de coopération internationale enables students to spend two months in developing countries working with community groups. The program introduces them to the development process and promotes intercultural understanding.

The Canadian International Development Agency helps fund this program.

More information is available from:

Centre canadien d'étude et de coopération internationale
180 Saint Catherine Street East
Montréal, QC   H2X 1K9
Tel: *(514) 875-9911*
Fax: *(514) 875-6469*
E-mail: *info@ceci.ca*
Web site: *www.ceci.ca*

CIDA's International Youth Internship Program

The objective of this program is to provide unemployed or under-employed Canadian youth with an opportunity to gain valuable international work experience in their field of study. Participants must be college or university graduates between 19 and 30 years of age.

The Canadian International Development Agency (CIDA) works with partner organizations (e.g., non-governmental organizations, colleges, universities, professional associations and the private sector) in Canada and abroad. Partner organizations select interns for overseas assignments and provide them with ongoing supervision and support.

Financed by the Government of Canada's Youth Employment Strategy, the program enables youth to contribute to CIDA's priorities in sustainable development by taking part in a 6- to 12-month internship — including a minimum of three months overseas.

For more information, contact:

CIDA Public Enquiries
Tel: *(819) 997-5006* (National Capital Region)
Toll-free: *1 800 230-6349*
TTY/TDD: *(819) 953-5023*
E-mail: *info@acdi-cida.gc.ca*
Web site: *www.acdi-cida.gc.ca/youth*

Co-op Program in International Development Studies

The University of Toronto at Scarborough offers a five-year under-graduate Co-op Program in International Development Studies (IDS Co-op). The program combines academic study in both social and environmental sciences with a co-op work placement in a developing country during the fourth year of study. Students work as development interns for 8 to 12 months with a non-governmental organization (usually Canadian) or one of their local development partners.

Placement costs are shared by the Canadian International Development Agency, the University of Toronto and the employer. Students return to Canada to complete their fifth and final year as well as a major research project initiated during their overseas placement. IDS Co-op students graduate with an Honours B.A. or B.Sc. with a Specialist Certificate in International Development Studies.

For further information, please check the IDS Co-op Web site, call the IDS Coordinator or mail inquiries to:

IDS Co-op Program — Division of Social Sciences
University of Toronto at Scarborough
1265 Military Trail
Scarborough, ON M1C 1A4
Tel: *(416) 287-7113*
Fax: *(416) 287-7283*
E-mail: *maxwell@scar.utoronto.ca*
Web site: *www.scar.utoronto.ca/~ids*

 # Finnish Career Development Exchange Program

This program is designed for young Canadian workers who have graduated in disciplines related to information technology, forestry or teaching English/French as a foreign language.

If you are a Canadian citizen between 18 and 30 years of age, have a post-secondary degree or diploma, an adequate knowledge of English, Finnish, Swedish, French or German, and at least one year of work experience directly related to your field of study, you can apply for a work exchange of up to 18 months in Finland in an area related to your field of study.

You will gain professional experience and have the opportunity to learn about the values and culture of Finland. The Finnish government will do a job search on your behalf but you should also attempt to find a job on your own. You are responsible for your own travel and living expenses. Applications are accepted until February 15.

For more information and an application form, contact:

International Youth Experience
12 Laval Street
Aylmer, QC J9H 1C5
Tel: *(819) 684-9212*
Fax: *(819) 684-5630*
E-mail: *jp.larochelle@experience.qc.ca*
Web site: *www.experience.qc.ca*

International Environmental Youth Corps – Internships for Young Canadians

As part of the Government of Canada's Youth Employment Strategy, the International Environmental Youth Corps is a program initiated by the federal Minister of the Environment in partnership with the Canadian Council for Human Resources in the Environment Industry. It is designed to place young Canadians in international internships within the Canadian environment industry sector, which includes private companies, non-governmental organizations and academia.

If you are a graduate of a Canadian college or university, are under the age of 30 and would like to work in the environment industry, **contact**:

Canadian Council for Human Resources in the Environment Industry
Tel: *1 800 890-1924* (toll-free)
Web site: *www.ec.gc.ca/etad/ieyc_e.html* (Environment Canada)

Junior Professional Officers Program

Through this program, the Canadian International Development Agency supports the employment of young Canadians in the United Nations development system.

The aims of the program are to strengthen the United Nations system by increasing the number of Canadians involved, to facilitate the entrance of young Canadians into a system that is difficult to enter and to provide internationally minded young Canadian professionals with experience in managing development programs.

More information is available from:

Canadian International Development Agency
Public Inquiries Communications Branch
200 Promenade du Portage
Hull, QC K1A 0G4
Tel: *(819) 997-5006*
Fax: *(819) 953-6088*
TTY/TDD: *(819) 953-5023*
E-mail: *Info@acdi-cida.gc.ca*
Web site: *www.acdi-cida.gc.ca*

NetCorps Canada International

NetCorps Canada International offers young Canadians the opportunity to participate in exciting information and communication technology internships in developing countries in Asia, Central and Eastern Europe, Latin America, and Africa.

NetCorps Interns will offer technical support and advice on getting connected to the Internet, Web site construction and maintenance, software use and development, databases, networking, and much more. Each assignment is tailored to meet the specific needs of the host organization.

For more information, you can visit the Web site or contact the NetCorps Canada International Secretariat.

Tel: *(514) 931-9306*
Toll-free: *1 800 605-3526*
E-mail: *secretariat@netcorps-cyberjeunes.org*
Web site: *www.netcorps-cyberjeunes.org*

Office franco-québécois pour la jeunesse : Youth Employment Mobility

If you are between 18 and 35 years of age, a permanent resident of Canada, and have lived in Quebec for at least the past year, you may be eligible for the Youth Employment Mobility program. This youth employment exchange program enables young people to fully integrate into a living and working environment by providing them with a training experience in France.

The minimum stay is 6 months and the maximum is 12 months. Candidates must submit a work contract signed by a French employer on a special form provided by the Ministère de l'Emploi et de la Solidarité, Direction de la Population et des Migrations (France). Employment must be based on:

- a firm contract of at least 6 months (12 months maximum),
- a full-time job,
- a guaranteed fixed remuneration in keeping with the current wage for the occupation concerned and no less than the minimum guaranteed inter-occupational wage — apart from commission work, and
- wage and working conditions that conform to existing collective agreements or labour standards legislation.

For more information, contact:

Office franco-québécois pour la jeunesse
1441 René-Lévesque West, Room 301
Montréal, QC H3G 1T7
Tel: *(514) 873-4255*
Toll-free: *1 800 465-4255*
Fax: *(514) 873-0067*
E-mail: *info@ofqj.gouv.qc.ca*
Web site: *www.ofqj.gouv.qc.ca*

Program for North American Mobility in Higher Education

This program supports the development of international joint projects undertaken by consortium partnerships of institutions in Canada, the United States and Mexico to enhance student mobility. Student work placement is also possible. In Canada, the program is funded by Human Resources Development Canada and administered jointly with the Department of Foreign Affairs and International Trade.

Projects are undertaken by a consortium of universities, colleges and technical institutions. Participating students do not apply directly but are selected by the post-secondary institutions involved in a project under the program.

Program guidelines are available from:

Learning and Literacy Directorate
Human Resources Development Canada
Hull, QC K1A 0M5
Tel: *(819) 997-3362*
Fax: *(819) 953-5954*
E-mail: *tom.mccloskey@hrdc-drhc.gc.ca*
Web site: *www.hrdc-drhc.gc.ca*

Programme Coopérant-Volontaire

The Programme Coopérant-Volontaire is a training program for young francophone Canadians between the ages of 22 and 32 who have graduated from college or university and are interested in gaining international work or volunteer experience in a developing country.

This program comprises two 15-week sessions. The first involves in-class work that takes place at Cégep de Rivière-du-Loup in Quebec. The second session consists of a placement in West Africa (Mali, Burkina Faso) aimed primarily at giving young interns international work experience in their field of study.

The program addresses the growing demand for internationally experienced graduates in the Canadian workforce. This will benefit not only non-governmental organizations but also the private and public sectors as well as educational institutions. Other benefits include further development of the voluntary sector as well as the personal and professional development of these young students.

The Programme Coopérant-Volontaire is part of the international co-operation college curriculum and is recognized by the Ministry of Education in Quebec.

For more information, contact:

Service de la Formation Continue
Programme Coopérant-Volontaire
Cégep de Rivière-du-Loup
80 rue Frontenac
Rivière-du-Loup, QC G5R 1R1
Tel: *(819) 862-6903*
Web site: *www.cegep-rdl.qc.ca/coop.htm*

Youth International

As part of the Government of Canada's Youth Employment Strategy, Youth International provides out-of-school youth with an internationally focused work experience that can lead to long-term employment or self-employment.

You are eligible to apply if you are a young person (normally up to the age of 30), unemployed or underemployed, out of school and legally entitled to work in Canada.

For more information, contact your local Human Resources Development Canada office.

To find out how to become a sponsor or employer for Youth Internship Canada's Youth International program, fax the Public Enquiries Centre to order your copy of the Youth International Guide for Sponsors (Cat. No. Y205-2-07-98).

Human Resources Development Canada
Public Enquiries Centre
140 Promenade du Portage
Hull, QC K1A 0J9
Fax: *(819) 953-7260*

🔆 Youth International Internship Program

As part of the Government of Canada's Youth Employment Strategy, the Youth International Internship Program provides unemployed or underemployed Canadian youth with their first paid, career-related international work experience. The program helps out-of-school youth make the transition from school to the workplace. Participating youth must be Canadian citizens or permanent residents between 18 and 30 years of age.

To participate, eligible youth apply directly to sponsoring organizations that have projects.

To obtain a list of sponsoring organizations, or **for more information**, call toll-free or check out the program on the Department of Foreign Affairs and International Trade Web site.

Tel: *1 800 559-2888*
Web site: *www.dfait-maeci.gc.ca/interns/*

Need a passport? Want to know how to go about getting one? Turn to the *Travel* section of this publication for information on obtaining – and protecting – your passport.

Important Addresses and Phone Numbers

Please note that only regional office phone and/or fax numbers are provided in this index, when available, since these offices are not generally included in the program or service listing. To find Government of Canada addresses not listed here, check the Government of Canada section of your local telephone directory.

Agence Québec/Wallonie-Bruxelles pour la jeunesse
1441 Réne-Lévesque Boulevard
West, Room 301
Montréal, Quebec H3G 1T7

Agriculture and Agri-Food Canada – Research Branch
Sir John Carling Building
930 Carling Avenue
Ottawa, Ontario K1A 0C7

Apparel Human Resources Council
130 Slater Street, Suite 1050
Ottawa, Ontario K1P 6E2

Association internationale des étudiants en sciences économiques et commerciales
8 King Street East, Suite 208
Toronto, Ontario M5C 1B5

Association of Canadian Community Colleges
1223 Michael Street North
Suite 200
Ottawa, Ontario K1J 7T2

Association of Canadian Universities for Northern Studies
17 York Street, Suite 405
Ottawa, Ontario K1N 9J6

Association of Universities and Colleges of Canada
Canadian Awards Program
350 Albert Street, Suite 600
Ottawa, Ontario K1R 1B1

Association Québec-France
9 Place Royale
Québec, Quebec G1K 4G2

Atlantic Canada Opportunities Agency
The John Cabot Building
10 Barter's Hill, 11th Floor
PO Box 1060, Station C
St. John's, Newfoundland A1C 5M5

Youth Ventures Program
175 Airport Boulevard
Gander, Newfoundland A1V 1W5

Biotechnology Human Resource Council
130 Albert Street, Suite 420
Ottawa, Ontario K1P 5G4

Business Development Bank of Canada
5 Place Ville Marie, Suite 400
Montréal, Quebec H3B 5E7

Canada Career Consortium
66 Slater Street, Suite 1204
Ottawa, Ontario K1P 5H1

Canada Council for the Arts
350 Albert Street
PO Box 1047
Ottawa, Ontario K1P 5V8

Canada Economic Development for Quebec Regions
Tour de la Bourse
800 Victoria Square, Suite 3800
PO Box 247
Montréal, Quebec H4K 1E8

Canada Mortgage and Housing Corporation
700 Montréal Road
Ottawa, Ontario K1A 0P7

Canada's SchoolNet
Industry Canada
155 Queen Street, 4th Floor
Ottawa, Ontario K1A 0H5

Canada WorkinfoNET
240 Catherine Street, Suite 110
Ottawa, Ontario K2P 2G8

Canada World Youth
2330 Notre-Dame Street West
3rd Floor
Montréal, Quebec H3J 1N4

Canadian Association of University Teachers of German
Workstudent Program
Department of Germanic and Slavic
 Studies, Brock University
St. Catharines, Ontario L2S 3A1

Canadian Bureau for International Education
Canadian Awards Division
220 Laurier Avenue West
Suite 1100
Ottawa, Ontario K1P 5Z9

Canadian Council for Human Resources in the Environment Industry
700 4th Avenue SW, Suite 1450
Calgary, Alberta T2P 3J4

Canadian Crossroads International
31 Madison Avenue
Toronto, Ontario M5R 2S2

Canadian Film and Television Production Association
151 Slater Street, Suite 605
Ottawa, Ontario K1P 5H3

Canadian Foundation for Economic Education
2 St. Clair Avenue West, Suite 501
Toronto, Ontario M4V 1L5

Canadian 4-H Council
Central Experimental Farm
930 Carling Avenue, Building 26
Ottawa, Ontario K1A 0C6

Department of Canadian Heritage
Ottawa, Ontario K1A 0M5

Canadian International Development Agency
Public Enquiries/Communications
200 Promenade du Portage
Hull, Quebec K1A 0G4

Canadian National
935 de la Gauchetière Street West
Montréal, Quebec H3B 2M9

Canadian Space Agency
6767 Route de l'Aéroport
Saint-Hubert, Quebec J3Y 8Y9

Canadian Technology Human Resources Board

251 Bank Street, Suite 201
Ottawa, Ontario K2P 1X3

Canadian Tourism Human Resource Council

170 Laurier Avenue West
Suite 1104
Ottawa, Ontario K1P 5V5

CANDO

10404 66th Avenue, Suite 200
Edmonton, Alberta T6H 5R6

CanLearn Interactive

CanLearn Information Products
 Group
25 Eddy Street, 10th Floor
Room 110A25
Hull, Quebec K1A 0M5

Capilano College

2055 Purcell Way
North Vancouver, British Columbia
V7J 3H5

Career Edge

155 University Avenue, Suite 1650
Toronto, Ontario M5K 3B7

Carrefour de solidarité internationale

555 Short Street
Sherbrooke, Quebec J1H 2E6

Centre canadien d'étude et de coopération internationale

180 Saint Catherine Street East
Montréal, Quebec H2X 1K9

Cultural Human Resources Council

17 York Street, Suite 201
Ottawa, Ontario K1N 9J6

Environment Canada – Science Horizons Youth Internship Program

Regional/Service Offices

Atlantic Region
45 Alderney Drive, 16th Floor
Dartmouth, Nova Scotia B2Y 2N6
Fax: (902) 426-6434

National Capital Region
Place Vincent Massey
351 St. Joseph Boulevard
Hull, Quebec K1A 0H3
Fax: (819) 994-4396 (Ecosystems
  and Environmental Resources)
  8th Floor
  (819) 994-1691 (Environmental
  Quality Branch) 8th Floor
  (819) 953-0550 (Science Policy
  Branch) 7th Floor
  (819) 953-9029 (Environmental
  Protection Service) 18th Floor

Ontario Region
Office of the Regional Science
  Advisor
4905 Dufferin Street
Toronto, Ontario M3H 5T4
Fax: (416) 739-4691

Pacific and Yukon Region
Human Resources
700–1200 West 73rd Avenue
Vancouver, British Columbia
V6P 6H9
Fax: (604) 664-9168

Prairie and Northern Region
Environmental Conservation Branch
2365 Albert Street, Room 300
Regina, Saskatchewan S4P 4K1
Fax: (306) 780-7614

Quebec Region
Canadian Wildlife Service
1141 Route de l'Église, 9th Floor
PO Box 10100
Sainte-Foy, Quebec G1V 4H5
Fax: (418) 649-6475

Atmospheric Environment Service
Atmospheric and Climate Science
  Directorate
4905 Dufferin Street
Downsview, Ontario M3H 5T4
Fax: (416) 739-4265

*Environmental Monitoring and
  Assessment Network (EMAN)
  EMAN Co-ordinating Office*
867 Lakeshore Road
Burlington, Ontario L7R 4A6
Fax: (905) 336-4499

National Water Research Institute
PO Box 5050
Burlington, Ontario L7R 4A6
Fax: (905) 336-4989

National Wildlife Research Centre
100 Gamelin Boulevard
Hull, Quebec K1A 0H3
Fax: (819) 994-2917

Experience Canada
646 Principale Avenue
Gatineau, Quebec J8T 5L4

Export Development Corporation
151 O'Connor Street
Ottawa, Ontario K1A 1K3

Fisheries and Oceans Canada
200 Kent Street
13th Floor, Station 13228
Ottawa, Ontario K1A 0E6

Department of Foreign Affairs and International Trade
125 Sussex Drive
Ottawa, Ontario K1A 0G2

Forum for International Trade Training
30 Metcalfe Street, 4th Floor
Ottawa, Ontario K1P 5L4

Forum for Young Canadians
124 O'Connor Street, Suite 400
Ottawa, Ontario K1P 5M9

Health Canada – Childhood and Youth Division
Health Promotions and Programs
  Branch
Address Locator: 1909C2
Ottawa, Ontario K1A 1B4

Horticultural Human Resource Council
Regional Offices
British Columbia Region
203A–15225 104th Avenue
Surrey, British Columbia V3R 6Y8
Tel: (604) 588-1958

Quebec Region
Institut québécois des ressources
  humaines en horticulture
570 boulevard Roland Therrien
bureau 206
Longueuil, Quebec J4H 3V9
Tel: (450) 679-8810

National Office & Atlantic Region
131 Kee Road
Keswick Ridge, New Brunswick
E6L 1V3
Tel: (506) 363-3310

Ontario Region
7856 Fifth Line South
RR #4, Station Main
Milton, Ontario L9T 2X8
Tel: (905) 875-1805

House of Commons Page Programme (Recruitment)
Financial and Human Resources
  Services Directorate
Wellington Building, Room 538
Ottawa, Ontario K1A 0A6

Human Resources Development Canada
Ottawa, Ontario K1A 0M5

Regional Offices
Alberta and Northwest Territories
Canada Place
9700 Jasper Avenue, Suite 1440
Edmonton, Alberta T5J 4C1

British Columbia and Yukon
Library Square Tower
300 West Georgia Street, 15th Floor
Vancouver, British Columbia
V6B 6G3

Manitoba
Paris Building
259 Portage Avenue, Room 500
Winnipeg, Manitoba R3B 3L4

New Brunswick
615 Prospect Street West
PO Box 2600
Fredericton, New Brunswick
E3B 5V6

Newfoundland
689 Topsail Road
PO Box 12051
St. John's, Newfoundland A1B 3Z4

Nova Scotia
99 Wyse Road
PO Box 1350
Dartmouth, Nova Scotia B2Y 4B9

Ontario
4900 Yonge Street, 8th Floor
Willowdale, Ontario M2N 6A8

Prince Edward Island
85 Fitzroy Street
PO Box 8000
Charlottetown, Prince Edward
  Island C1A 8K1

Quebec
1441 St. Urbain Street, 8th Floor
Montréal, Quebec H2X 2M6

Saskatchewan
2101 Scarth Street
Regina, Saskatchewan S4P 2H9

Human Resources Development Canada – Office of Learning Technologies
15 Eddy Street, Ground Floor
Hull, Quebec K1A 0M5

Human Resources Development Canada – Public Enquiries Centre
140 Promenade du Portage
Phase IV
Hull, Quebec K1A 0J9

Department of Indian Affairs and Northern Development
Terrasses de la Chaudière
10 Wellington Street
Hull, Quebec

Postal Address: Ottawa, Ontario
K1A 0H4

Regional Offices

Alberta
630 Canada Place
9700 Jasper Avenue
Edmonton, Alberta T5J 4G2

Atlantic
40 Havelock Street
PO Box 160
Amherst, Nova Scotia B4H 3Z3

British Columbia
1550 Alberni Street, Suite 340
Vancouver, British Columbia
V6G 3C5

Manitoba
275 Portage Avenue, Room 1100
Winnipeg, Manitoba R3B 3A3

*Northwest Territories and Eastern
  Arctic*
PO Box 1500
Yellowknife, Northwest Territories
X1A 2R3

Ontario
Arthur Meighen Building
25 St. Clair Avenue East, 5th Floor
Toronto, Ontario M4T 1M2

Quebec
PO Box 51127
320 St. Joseph Street East
Postal Outlet G. Roy
Québec, Quebec G1K 8Z7

Saskatchewan
2221 Cornwall Street, Room 301
Regina, Saskatchewan S4P 4M2

Yukon
300 Main Street, Suite 345
Whitehorse, Yukon Y1A 2B5

Industry Canada
155 Queen Street
Ottawa, Ontario K1A 0H5

Industry Canada – Entrepreneurship and Small Business Office
235 Queen Street
Ottawa, Ontario K1A 0H5

International Council for Canadian Studies
325 Dalhousie Street, Suite 800
Ottawa, Ontario K1N 7G2

International Development Research Centre
PO Box 8500
Ottawa, Ontario K1G 3H9

International Youth Experience
12 Laval Street
Aylmer, Quebec J9H 1C5

Inuit Tapirisat of Canada
170 Laurier Avenue West, Suite 510
Ottawa, Ontario K1P 5V5

Department of Justice Canada
Ottawa, Ontario K1A 0H8

Library of Parliament
Ottawa, Ontario K1A 0A9

MazeMaster – Project Staff
c/o Toronto District Catholic School
  Board
80 Sheppard Avenue East
Toronto, Ontario M2N 6E8

Medical Research Council of Canada
Holland Cross, Tower B
1600 Scott Street, 5th Floor
Postal Locator: 3105A
Ottawa, Ontario K1A 0W9

Important Addresses and Phone Numbers

Métis National Council
350 Sparks Street, Suite 201
Delta Hotel Office Tower
Ottawa, Ontario K1R 7S8

National Aboriginal Achievement Foundation
70 Yorkville Avenue, Suite 33A
Toronto, Ontario M5R 1B9

National Association of Friendship Centres
275 MacLaren Street
Ottawa, Ontario K2P 0L9

Department of National Defence – Headquarters
Major General Georges R. Pearkes
  Building
101 Colonel By Drive
Ottawa, Ontario K1A 0K2

National Life/Work Centre
Memramcook Institute
PO Box 180
Saint-Joseph, New Brunswick
E0A 2Y0

National Research Council of Canada
Montréal Road
Ottawa, Ontario K1A 0R6

National Seafood Sector Council
85 Albert Street, Suite 1505
Ottawa, Ontario K1P 6A4

National Transportation Week
451 Daly Avenue
Ottawa, Ontario K1N 6H6

Natural Resources Canada
580 Booth Street
Ottawa, Ontario K1A 0E4

Natural Resources Canada – Earth Sciences Sector
601 Booth Street
Ottawa, Ontario K1A 0E8

NSERC (the Natural Sciences and Engineering Research Council of Canada)
Scholarships and Fellowships
  Division
350 Albert Street
Ottawa, Ontario K1A 1H5

Office franco-québécois pour la jeunesse
1441 René-Lévesque Boulevard
  West, Room 301
Montréal, Quebec H3G 1T7

Office of Learning Technologies
Human Resources Development
  Canada
15 Eddy Street, Ground Floor
Hull, Quebec K1A 0M5

Passport Office
Ottawa, Ontario K1A 0G3

Public Service Commission of Canada
Regional Offices
Alberta
9700 Jasper Avenue, Suite 830
Edmonton, Alberta T5J 4G3
Tel: (403) 495-7444 (Edmonton)
Tel: (403) 292-4333 (Calgary)
Tel: (403) 340-4232 (Red Deer)
TTY: (403) 495-3130
Fax: (403) 495-3145

Atlantic
777 Main Street, 7th Floor
Moncton, New Brunswick E1C 1E9
Tel: (506) 851-6616
TTY: (506) 851-6624
Fax: (506) 851-6618

Baine Johnston Centre
10 Fort William Road, 1st Floor
St. John's, Newfoundland A1C 1K4
Tel: (709) 772-4812
TTY: (709) 772-4317
Fax: (709) 772-4316

Ralston Building
1557 Hollis Street, 3rd Floor
PO Box 1664 (CRO)
Halifax, Nova Scotia B3J 3V3
Tel: (902) 426-2990
TTY: (902) 426-6246
Fax: (902) 426-0507

119 Kent Street, Suite 420
Charlottetown, Prince Edward
 Island C1A 1N3
Tel: (902) 368-0444
TTY: (902) 566-7039
Fax: (902) 566-7036

British Columbia
Sinclair Centre
757 Hastings Street West, Suite 210
Vancouver, British Columbia
V6C 3M2
Tel: (604) 666-0350
TTY: (604) 666-6868
Fax: (604) 666-6808

1230 Government Street
Room 539
Victoria, British Columbia
V8W 3M4
Tel: (250) 363-8120
TTY: (250) 363-0564
Fax: (250) 363-0558

Manitoba
344 Edmonton Street, Suite 100
Winnipeg, Manitoba R3B 2L4
Tel: (204) 984-4636
TTY: (204) 983-6066
Fax: (204) 983-8188

National Capital Region and
 Eastern Ontario
66 Slater Street, 3rd Floor
Ottawa, Ontario K1A 0M7
Tel: (613) 996-8436
TTY: (613) 996-1205
Fax: (613) 996-8048

Northwest Territories
Bellanca Building
4914 50th Street, 3rd floor
Yellowknife, Northwest Territories
X1A 2R1
Tel: (403) 669-2840
Fax: (403) 669-2848

Ontario
1 Front Street West, 6th Floor
Toronto, Ontario M5J 2X5
Tel: (416) 973-4636
TTY: (416) 973-2269
Fax: (416) 973-1883

Quebec
Champlain Harbour Station
901 Cap Diamant, 3rd Floor
Québec, Quebec G1S 1E5
Tel: (418) 648-3230
TTY: (418) 648-7273
Fax: (418) 648-4575

Complexe Guy Favreau
East Tower, 8th Floor
200 René-Lévesque Boulevard West
Montréal, Quebec H2Z 1X4
Tel: (514) 283-5776
TTY: (514) 283-2467
Fax: (514) 496-2404

Saskatchewan
1955 Smith Street, Suite 400
Regina, Saskatchewan S4P 2N8
Tel: (306) 780-5627
TTY: (306) 780-6719
Fax: (306) 780-5723

Yukon
300 Main Street, Suite 400
Whitehorse, Yukon Y1A 2B5
Tel: (867) 667-3900
Jobline: (867) 667-4678
Fax: (867) 668-5033

Senate of Canada – Page Program
Human Resources Directorate
Parliament Buildings
Ottawa, Ontario K1N 0A4

Shad International
8 Young Street East
Waterloo, Ontario N2J 2L3

Social Insurance Number (SIN) Registration
PO Box 7000
Bathurst, New Brunswick E2A 4T1

Social Sciences and Humanities Research Council of Canada
Fellowships
350 Albert Street
PO Box 1610
Ottawa, Ontario K1P 6G4

Software Human Resource Council
30 Metcalfe Street, Suite 400
Ottawa, Ontario K1P 5L4

Textiles Human Resources Council
66 Slater Street, Suite 1720
Ottawa, Ontario K1P 5H1

Volunteer Canada
430 Gilmour Street
Ottawa, Ontario K2P 0R8

WITT National Network
830 Bathurst Street
Toronto, Ontario M5R 3G1

Internet Index

Every effort has been made to ensure that the sites listed in this index are accessible at the addresses indicated. If you are having problems accessing a site, contact the organization involved for changes to the URL for the Web site. Information on other means of contacting specific departments or organizations is provided in the related program or service descriptions within this publication. Use the Index by Organization and Program Listing and/or the Subject Index to locate specific listings.

Aboriginal Business Canada
http://abc.gc.ca

Aboriginal Youth Network
www.ayn.ca

Accelerated Economist Training Program
www.psc-cfp.gc.ca/aetp/aetp.htm

Agriculture and Agri-Food Canada
www.agr.ca

Apparel Human Resource Council
www.apparel-hrc.org

Apply to Teach Network
www.attn.org

Association internationale des étudiants en sciences économiques et commerciales
www.ca.aiesec.org

Association of Canadian Community Colleges
www.accc.ca

Association of Canadian Universities for Northern Studies
http://aix1.uottawa.ca/associations/aucen-acuns

Association of Universities and Colleges of Canada
www.aucc.ca

Atlantic Canada Opportunities Agency
www.acoa.ca

Biotechnology Human Resource Council
www.bhrc.ca

Business Development Bank of Canada
www.bdc.ca

Cadets Canada
www.cadetscanada.org

Campus WorkLink
www.campusworklink.com

Canada Career Consortium
www.careerccc.org

Canada Council for the Arts
www.canadacouncil.ca

Canada Customs and Revenue Agency
www.ccra-adrc.gc.ca

Canada Customs and Revenue Agency – Tax Information for Students
www.ccra-adrc.gc.ca/menu/EmenuGNN.html

Canada Economic Development for Quebec Regions
www.dec-ced.gc.ca

Canada Education Savings Grant
http://hrdc-drhc.gc.ca/cesg

Canada Mortgage and Housing Corporation
www.cmhc-schl.gc.ca

Canada Pension Plan
www.hrdc-drhc.gc.ca/isp/

Canada's Digital Collections Program
http://collections.ic.gc.ca

Canada's SchoolNet
www.schoolnet.ca

Canada Student Loans Program
www.hrdc-drhc.gc.ca/student_loans

Canada's Youth Employment Strategy
www.youth.gc.ca/YES/

Canada WorkinfoNET
www.workinfonet.ca

Canada World Youth
www.cwy-jcm.org

Canadian Aquaculture Industry Alliance Sector Council
www.aquaculture.ca

Canadian Association of Equipment Distributors
www.caed.org

Canadian Automotive Repair and Service Council
www.cars-council.ca

Canadian Aviation Maintenance Council
www.camc.ca

Canadian Bureau for International Education
www.cbie.ca

Canadian Conservation Institute
www.cci-icc.gc.ca

Canadian Council for Human Resources in the Environment Industry
www.cchrei.org

Canadian Council of Professional Engineers
www.ccpe.ca/

Canadian Council of Professional Fish Harvesters
www.ccpfh-ccpp.org

Canadian Crossroads International
www.crossroads-carrefour.ca

Canadian Film and Television Production Association
www.cftpa.ca

Canadian Foundation for Economic Education
www.cfee.org

Canadian 4-H Council
www.4-h-canada.ca

Department of Canadian Heritage
www.pch.gc.ca

Canadian International Development Agency
www.acdi-cida.gc.ca

Canadian Museum of Civilization
www.civilization.ca/

Canadian Museum of Nature
www.nature.ca/

Canadian National
www.cn.ca

Canadian Professional Logistics Institute
www.loginstitute.ca

Canadian Space Agency
www.space.gc.ca/kidspace/index.html

Canadian Steel Trade and Employment Congress
www.cstec.ca

Canadian Technology Human Resources Board
www.cthrb.ca

Canadian Tourism Human Resource Council
www.cthrc.ca

Canadian Trucking Human Resources Council
www.cthrc.com

CANDO
www.edo.ca

CanLearn Interactive
www.canlearn.ca

Capilano College – APMCP/CANASEAN Exchange Program
www.capcollege.bc.ca/apmcp

Career Edge
www.careeredge.org

Career Mall
www.cpsa.com/html/career_mall.asp

Carrefour de solidarité internationale
www.csisher.com

Centre canadien d'étude et de coopération internationale
www.ceci.ca

Community Access Program
http://cap.ic.gc.ca/

Community Futures Development Corporations – Quebec
www.reseau-sadc.qc.ca

Computers for Schools
www.schoolnet.ca/cfs-ope

Conference Board of Canada
www.conferenceboard.ca/nbec

Contact! The Canadian Management Network
http://strategis.ic.gc.ca/contact

Contracts Canada
http://contractscanada.gc.ca

Cultural Human Resources Council
www.curlturalhrc.ca

Digital Collections Program
http://collections.ic.gc.ca

Electronic and Appliance Service Industry
www.easi.ca/easi

Electronic Labour Exchange
www.ele-spe.org

Environment Canada
www.ec.gc.ca

Experience Canada
www.experiencecanada.org

Export Development Corporation
www.edc.ca

Farm Credit Corporation
www.fcc-sca.ca

Federal Public Sector Youth Internship Program
www.careeredge.org

First Nations SchoolNet
www.schoolnet.ca/aboriginal

Fisheries and Oceans Canada
www.dfo-mpo.gc.ca/ssip

Department of Foreign Affairs and International Trade
www.dfait-maeci.gc.ca

Forum for International Trade Training
www.fitt.ca

Forum for Young Canadians
www.forum.ca

Government of Canada – Information
www.canada.gc.ca
www.gc.ca

Government of Canada – Publications
http://publications.pwgsc.gc.ca

Health Canada – Childhood and Youth Division
www.hc-sc.gc.ca/childhood-youth

House of Commons – Page Programme
www.parl.gc.ca/36/pp-e.htm

Human Resources Development Canada
www.hrdc-drhc.gc.ca

Human Resources Development Canada – Career Awareness Site
www.hrdc-drhc.gc.ca/career-carriere

Human Resources Development Canada – Job Futures
www.hrdc-drhc.gc.ca/JobFutures

Human Resources Development Canada – National Youth Mirror Site
http://youth.hrdc-drhc.gc.ca

Human Resources Development Canada – Office of Learning Technologies
http://olt-bta.hrdc-drhc.gc.ca

Human Resources Development Canada – Social Insurance Number Registration
www.hrdc-drhc.gc.ca/nas/nas2120e.shtml

Department of Indian Affairs and Northern Development
www.inac.gc.ca

Industry Canada
www.ic.gc.ca

Industry Canada – Strategis
http://strategis.ic.gc.ca

Information on the Government of Canada
www.canada.gc.ca

Information Technology Professional Program (Software Human Resource Council)
http://itp.shrc.ca

International Council for Canadian Studies
www.iccs-ciec.ca

International Development Research Centre
www.idrc.ca

International Development Studies Co-op Program
www.scar.utoronto.ca/~ids

International Environmental Youth Corps
www.ec.gc.ca/etad/ieyc_e.html

International Youth Experience
www.experience.qc.ca

Job Bank
http://jb-ge.hrdc-drhc.gc.ca

Job Mart – Canadian Aviation Maintenance Council
http://jobmart.camc.ca

Department of Justice Canada
http://canada.justice.gc.ca

Katimavik
www.katimavik.org

Labour Market Information Service
http://lmi-imt.hrdc-drhc.gc.ca

Library of Parliament
www.parl.gc.ca

Management Trainee Program
www.psc-cfp.gc.ca/mtp/index.htm

MazeMaster
www.mazemaster.on.ca

Medical Research Council of Canada
www.mrc.gc.ca

Mining Industry Training and Adjustment Council
www.mitac.ca

National Aboriginal Achievement Foundation
www.naaf.ca

National Association of Friendship Centres
www.nafc-aboriginal.com

Department of National Defence – Canadian Cadets
www.cadetscanada.org

National Gallery of Canada
www.gallery.ca

National Life/Work Centre
http://lifework.ca

National Museum of Science and Technology
www.nmstc.ca/

National Research Council
www.nrc.ca/careers

National Research Council – Industrial Research Assistance Program
www.nrc.ca/irap

National Seafood Sector Council
www.nssc.ca

Natural Resources Canada – Canadian Forest Service
www.nrcan.gc.ca/cfs

Natural Resources Canada – Science and Technology Internship Program
www.nrcan.gc.ca/css/hrsb/intern-e.htm

NetCorps Canada International
www.netcorps-cyberjeunes.org

Northern Scientific Training Program
www.inac.gc.ca/pubs/northern/nstp.html

NSERC (the Natural Sciences and Engineering Research Council of Canada)
www.nserc.ca

Nurses@work
www.nursesatwork.com

Office franco-québecois pour la jeunesse
www.ofqj.gouv.qc.ca

Office of Learning Technologies
http://olt-bta.hrdc-drhc.gc.ca

Open House Canada
www.pch.gc.ca/yp-pj/index.html

Packaging Careers Council of Canada
www.packagingcareers.org

Parliament of Canada
www.parl.gc.ca

Passport Office
www.ppt.gc.ca

Post-Secondary Recruitment for the Federal Public Service
http://jobs.gc.ca

Programme Coopérant-Volontaire – Cégep de Rivière-du-Loup
www.cegep-rdl.qc.ca/coop.htm

Public Service Commission of Canada
www.psc-cfp.gc.ca

Public Service Commission of Canada – Recruitment
http://jobs.gc.ca

Public Works and Government Services Canada
www.pwgsc.gc.ca

Public Works and Government Services Canada – Publications
http://publications.pwgsc.gc.ca

The Real Game
www.realgame.ca

REALM: Creating Work You Want
http://realm.net

Retail Council of Canada
www.retailcouncil.org

Royal Canadian Mounted Police
www.rcmp-grc.gc.ca

SchoolNet
www.schoolnet.ca

SchoolNet GrassRoots Program
www.schoolnet.ca/grassroots

SchoolNet News Network
www.schoolnet.ca/snn

SchoolNet Youth Employment Initiative
www.schoolnet.ca/yei

SkillNet.ca
www.skillnet.ca

Social Sciences and Humanities Research Council of Canada
www.sshrc.ca

Software Career Discovery Centre
www.discoverIT.org

Software Human Resource Council
www.shrc.ca

Strategis
http://strategis.ic.gc.ca

Student Connection Program
www.scp-ebb.com

Student Need Assessment Software
http://205.207.175.25/cgi-bin/hrdcsnas/snasen.html
www.canlearn.ca/english/fin/debtfreeguide/csl/hrdcsnas/
   snasen.shtml

Talent Gallery – Cultural Human Resources Council
www.culturalhrc.ca

Technology First Work Placement Service
www.cthrb.ca/1tech/

Textiles Human Resources Council
www3.sympatico.ca/thrc

Transport Canada
www.tc.gc.ca

Treasury Board Secretariat
www.tbs-sct.gc.ca

Volunteer Canada
www.volunteer.ca

Volunteer Opportunities Exchange
www.voe-reb.org

Western Economic Diversification Canada
www.wd.gc.ca

WITT (Women in Trades and Technology) National Network
www.wittnn.com/works

WorkSearch
www.worksearch.gc.ca

You Corp.
www.you-corp.com

Young Canada Works
www.pch.gc.ca/ycw-jct/

Your Guide to Government of Canada Services and Support for Small Business
http://strategis.ic.gc.ca

Youth Employment Strategy
www.youth.gc.ca/YES/

Youth Info Fairs
http://youth.hrdc-drhc.gc.ca/publication/youthfr.shtml

Youth International Internship Program
www.dfait-maeci.gc.ca/youth

Youth Resource Network of Canada
www.youth.gc.ca

Index by Organization and Program Listing

Forum for International Trade Training

Forum for Young Canadians

Health Canada

Horticultural Human Resources Council

House of Commons

Human Resources Development Canada

Department of Indian Affairs and Northern Development

Industry Canada

International Council for Canadian Studies

International Development Research Centre

Subject Index

H

Harvard University, graduate fellowships 27

House of Commons Page Programme 160

Housing Internship Initiative for First Nations and Inuit Youth 161

Human Resources Development Canada Offices 101

Human Resources Development Canada Offices for Students 101

I

IDEA-SME, business support 90

IDRC Doctoral Research Awards 30

Imasco Scholarship Fund for Disabled Students 31

income tax, help with filing 77, 80

India, Commonwealth scholarship 19

Information Highway Science and Entrepreneurship Camps 161

Information on the Government of Canada 117

Information Technology Professional Program 117

information tools, career 47–72

international development
awards for graduate research 3, 5, 17, 26, 30, 37
career information 56
jobs/internships/student exchanges 149,194, 200, 201, 202, 203, 204, 206, 207, 209

International Environmental Youth Corps – Internships for Young Canadians 206

International 4-H Trade Awareness Program 132

International Space University Summer Session 32

International Trade Personnel Program 162

Internship Programs in Film and Television Production 163

internships
abroad 189, 194–211
agriculture 196, 199
apparel manufacturing 173
art galleries/museums 158, 186
computer science/informatics 150, 159, 168, 172, 173, 174, 207
co-op 151, 157, 158, 184, 197, 202, 204
culture/heritage 152, 158, 185, 197, 198, 200, 205
defence/security 152
engineering 172, 173, 174, 182, 184
environment 174, 187, 204, 206
film and television production 163
horticulture 171
international development 149, 194, 200, 201, 202, 203, 204, 206, 207, 209
marine and oceanic science 174
marketing 150, 161, 162, 166, 173, 174, 175, 179
media/communications 158, 161, 166, 170, 185-188
national parks/historic sites 187
official languages 167, 176, 185
public service 145, 151, 155, 159, 164, 168, 169, 180, 185
research and development 172

m

Make the Skills Connection, pamphlet 59

Management Trainee Program 164

Mandarin language, Taiwan study scholarship 8

Mattinson Endowment Fund Scholarship for Disabled Students 34

MazeMaster, career/job exploration tool 60

Meet the Sector Councils 61

Mexico
student mobility projects 209
study/research scholarship 26

Middle East, doctoral fieldwork 30

Minding Your Own Business, small-business information booklet 65

multimedia production, work experience in 147, 188

museums, work experience at 158, 186

music, grants and services for artists 29

n

National Aboriginal Capital Corporations Association 88

National Association of Friendship Centres 110

National Research Council Research Associateships Program 165

National Research Council Summer Employment Program 166

National Transportation Week 54

Native youth *see* Aboriginal youth

NetCorps Canada International 207

Netherlands, work in 199

New Zealand
Commonwealth scholarship 19
working holiday 139

Northern Scientific Training Program, Canada's 75

northern studies, awards program 10

NSERC Industrial Post-graduate Scholarships 35

NSERC Post-doctoral Fellowships 35

NSERC Post-graduate Scholarships 36

Nurses@work: Career Opportunities for Nurses 103

o

Obtaining a Passport 133

Office franco-québécois pour la jeunesse : Youth Employment Mobility 208

Office of Learning Technologies 121

Official Language Fellowships 37

Official Language Monitor Program 167

official languages
bursaries/scholarships 7, 34, 39, 42
fellowship 37
jobs 167, 185

How Are We Doing?

Your feedback will help us continue to meet the needs of our target audiences. Please take a minute to complete this form and return it to us by mail or fax. (Be sure to include your return address so we can send you a complimentary Youth Employment Strategy item!)

Which of the following describes you? (You may check off more than one item.)

❑ youth

    ❑ 15–19   ❑ 20–24   ❑ 25–29   ❑ 30+

❑ parent/guardian

❑ professional working with youth (please specify: _____)

❑ government organization

❑ non-government organization

❑ other (please specify: _____)

How did you get your copy of *Youth Link*?

(Please specify: _____)

How did you first find out about *Youth Link*?

❑ word-of-mouth

❑ on the Internet

❑ Human Resources Development Canada office

❑ other (please specify: _____)

How would you rate *Youth Link* overall?

❑ very useful

❑ somewhat useful

❑ not very useful

❑ useless

**How has the information provided in *Youth Link* helped you –
either directly or indirectly?** (Please be as specific and complete as
possible in your answer: has it helped you find a job? fine-tune
your job-search tactics? get a scholarship? start a business? get a
student loan? explore your career options? a combination of
these?)

_____

_____

_____

_____

_____

Comments/suggestions for improvement?

_____

_____

_____

_____

Thank you for taking the time to answer our questions. Please
return this questionnaire, along with your return address, to:

Youth Communications Directorate
Human Resources Development Canada
140 Promenade du Portage
Phase IV, 4th Floor
Hull, QC K1A 0J9
Fax: (819) 953-3186

Youth
Employment
Strategy

Stratégie
emploi
jeunesse

Return address (please print clearly):

Name: _____

Address: _____

City/Province: _____

Postal Code: _____

Notes

Notes

Notes

Notes

Notes